D1107697

Achieving Consensus on Water Policy in California

Other "Pat" Brown Institute Publications

OCCASIONAL PAPERS — ($5.00 ea.)

*Political Battles Over L.A. County Board Seats: A Minority Perspective. James A. Regalado, Editor (1989).

*Gang Violence Prevention: Perspectives and Strategies. Alfredo Gonzalez and Shirley Better, with Ralph Dawson (1990).

*Minority Political Empowerment. James A. Regalado, Editor (1991).

MONOGRAPHS — ($8.95 ea.)

*The Perfecting of Los Angeles: Ethics Reform on the Municipal Level. H. Eric Schockman, Editor (1989).

*Emergency Disaster Management: Patterns of Inter City Mutual Aid [L.A. County]. George C. Littke (1989).

Latino Public Employment and Political Representation in Los Angeles: 1968-1989. Tom Larson (1992)

BOOKS

*Twentieth-Century Los Angeles: Power, Promotion, and Social Conflict. Norman Klein and Martin Schiesl, Editors (1990). Paper ($14.50).

*California Initiatives and Referendums, 1912-1990: A Survey and Guide to Research. John M. Allswang (1991). Cloth ($29.95).

ORDER FROM

"Pat" Brown Institute
California State University, Los Angeles
Publications Sales Office
1100 Industrial Road, Suite 9
San Carlos, CA 94070

Achieving Consensus on Water Policy in California

EDMUND G.
"PAT" BROWN
INSTITUTE
OF PUBLIC AFFAIRS

Edmund G. "Pat" Brown Institute of Public Affairs
California State University, Los Angeles

Water Education Foundation
Sacramento, CA

10   9   8   7   6   5   4   3   2   1

ISBN: 1-878644-04-1

Edmund G. "Pat" Brown Institute of Public Affairs
California State University, Los Angeles, CA 90032

Manufactured in the United States of America.

PREFACE

Co-edited with the Water Education Foundation, in Sacramento, "Achieving Consensus on California Water Policy" is the eighth publication of the Edmund G. "Pat" Brown Institute of Public Affairs and, perhaps, typifies in a special way the scope and purpose of the Institute's publications program.

Founded in 1980 as an independent, non-partisan organization by friends and associates of Governor Brown on the occasion of his 75th birthday, the "Pat" Brown Institute has been affiliated with California State University, Los Angeles, since 1987. Its continuing mission is to create more effective means of communication between and among the public and private sectors, citizens and residents, culturally diverse communities, and scholars and students on important public policy issues.

To this end, the Institute offers a forum series and a publication series. These focus on four broad areas of research: Governance and Representation, Social Well-Being, Economy and the Infrastructure, and Natural Resources and the Environment.

In the latter category, as is frequently remarked upon by chapter authors in this volume, no single achievement of Pat Brown in his two terms as governor, 1959-1967, surpasses his leadership role in the development of California water resources and public policy. Indeed, his own Foreword, however modestly, reveals the nature and extend of his remarkable exercise of courageous political leadership as well as the challenges which remain in "Achieving Consensus on California Water Policy."

The publication of this volume was considerably eased along the way by several individuals whose contributions it is my pleasure to gratefully acknowledge: Rita Schmidt Sudman, Executive Director, Water Education Foundation, for her work with the individual chapter authors and general editorship of the book; Paul Youket, interim director of the "Pat" Brown Institute during the period when the volume was originally conceived and planned; Bill Stall, *Los Angeles Times* staff writer who provided an insightful and incisive evaluation of the manuscript based on his long experience in covering California politics and water wars; and Morris Polan, the Institute's publications consultant, who oversaw the final stages of editing and publication.

I should like to thank, also, the members of the Board of Advisors of the Edmund G. "Pat" Brown Institute of Public Affairs for their encouragement and support of our efforts to bring this project to fruition.

James A. (Jaime) Regalado, Ph.D.
Executive Director,
"Pat" Brown Institute

CONTENTS

Gov. Pat Brown signing into effect the California Water Plan as Assemblyman Carley Porter and DWR Director Bill Warne look on. Photo credit: Water Education Foundation.

FOREWORD

Edmund G. "Pat" Brown

Many Californians grew up with our own water problems, just as from its earliest history the state has grown up with the problems of conserving and redistributing the scant supplies of rain in the valleys and snow in the mountains that it receives each winter. Our personal experiences determine the depth of our appreciation of our common lot in this arid climate, but often these experiences differ and our disagreements, based on these differences, delay actions that are proposed in the interests of the greater community.

As a boy, I became conscious of the need to save and use wisely this controlling resource. In the summers, I visited the dry-farmed ranch that my grandparents had homesteaded. It lay behind the foothills of the Coast Range, 14 miles west of Williams. The creek that ran through the ranch was barely a trickle in August, but in most years in the spring it flooded some bottom land and then there was grass for the cattle. In dry years, pasture was scarce. Even as a young boy, I felt the anxiety that pervaded the whole valley during such droughts.

The ranch is still in the family. Although it has been 80 years since I first summered there, the ranch's thirst has never been slaked. The particular little valley in which the ranch is located is isolated from water sources, save only its inadequate and undependable creek. Its water supply cannot be augmented economically. Lack of irrigation has continued to limit the use of the land. The ranch, in its dusty beauty, will occasionally beckon a little boy from the city sidewalks to spend a few

Edmund G. "Pat" Brown served as governor of California from 1959 to 1966.

summer weeks saddling a horse in the corral and riding like a real cowboy over the sunbaked range, as I once did. It is my nostalgic hope that this may continue to be so.

But I, my children and their children, and my brother and cousins, and their children and grandchildren have had to make our livings elsewhere. None of us could be supported by the dry-farmed cattle spread. We all live and work in the cities where water is delivered to us by world-class pumping plants, through hundreds of miles of aqueducts. The projects that serve us were financed by the state or other public agencies, and they were built by expert engineers and craftsmen using 20th century technology. But some of us are still sentimental about the ranch, and we take pride in our continued ownership of it.

As a young man, I came to see that the control and management of the water resources of the state were essential in order to support and to sustain progress in California. Growth and development of California is and always has been dependent on the provision of dependable supplies of water to our cities, industries and farms. Wide annual variations and seasonal differences in rainfall, together with the fact that most of the rainfall comes in the north while the greatest need is in the south, provide the dimensions of our management problem, which has grown more complex as more of the resource is managed. If California's 104 million acres had been left unimproved, like my grandparents' ranch, probably no more than 4 million of our 30 million people could make their homes in California. We have one natural advantage, however, in seeking to control our water destiny. Our mountains save the winter snows until they are melted by the summer sun, just at the time that the dry valleys below are most in need of water to irrigate their crops. We have built more than 1,000 dams in the mountain canyons to form reservoirs to catch, conserve and distribute the floods and freshets that come at the time of snowmelt. These developments control something less than 60 percent of the normal annual average of 75 million acre-feet of water that accumulates in our rivers as a result of the winter storms. When we talk of agriculture using 80 percent of California's water, it is only the developed resource of which we speak. More than 40 percent of the total supply flows uncontrolled to the sea, serving fish and wildlife and other environmental purposes as it runs.

I followed with fascination the development of the Colorado River, thrilled with everyone at the construction of Boulder (now Hoover) Dam. And in the Depression years of the 1930s, I observed the gallant fight of California's water leaders to win approval of the Central Valley Project (CVP). I was encouraged when the federal government financed that project for construction by the Bureau of Reclamation. When I was attorney general I made my trips to Washington to assist in working out various problems that arose between the feds and the CVP water contractors in the interests of the state.

It was increasingly clear to me that as long as California continued to grow and develop, each generation would face and must resolve a new set of water problems. At intervals of about 30 years, the dynamics of the state's development had demanded new appraisals of recently created water needs. Renewed action to meet those needs became essential. A continuing series of water confrontations marked our history, dating back more than a century to the revolt of the farmers that put the hydraulic mining industry out of business in the gold fields. Hoover Dam, the Colorado River Aqueduct to the Los Angeles basin, San Francisco's Hetch Hetchy project, the CVP--each had been a riser on our stairs to the future.

When I first campaigned for governor in 1958, it had been almost 30 years since the CVP had been put forward. Bob Edmonston, who was in the state's water agency during the CVP fight, saw in the immediate future an emerging need for a grander and more comprehensive solution, one that would serve the cities as well as agriculture, which had been the main beneficiary of the CVP. He tutored me. I developed the campaign for the State Water Project. I emphasized the theme that California was "one state" and that its growing water needs were not solely local, nor were they only regional, but that together they made up a single problem that confronted the entire state, and I thought that they should be approached on that basis.

My eight-year administration was one of unrelenting effort to formulate and construct a statewide water project that would serve the needs of all of California for 30 years and that could be expanded simply by developing additional sources in order to serve the generations that would succeed us. Sen. Hugh Burns and

Assemblyman Carley Porter wrote the Burns-Porter Act to authorize issuance of $1.75 billion of bonds to finance the initial construction. The bond issue was approved by the people at the general election in November 1960. With the help of Harvey Banks and Bill Berry, who prepared the plan, and that of the superb team Bill Warne put together in the Department of Water Resources, we made the State Water Project a reality.

Gov. Pat Brown, 1989. Photo credit: Water Education Foundation.

We negotiated 30 water service contracts with entities serving water users throughout the state, including counties, cities and districts, some on the Feather River north of Sacramento, others both north and south of San Francisco Bay. Some contracts were with agricultural water users along the west side of the San Joaquin Valley and in Kern County, and some that involved about half of the project's water were with the growing urban districts in southern California. These 30 water service contractors provide some or all of the water requirements of two-thirds of the people of the state of California. The contractors agreed to repay the costs of construction, operation and maintenance of the project, and I am happy to observe that they regularly have met their obligations with payments that now have reached totals running to billions of dollars.

We then turned our attention to construction. We built Oroville Dam and much of the California Aqueduct while I was governor. We resolved unique technical problems. We designed and built the pumping plant of unprecedented dimensions at the Tehachapi Crossing to deliver more water through a higher lift than had ever before been attempted by man. We did these things while the engineering world watched and frequently applauded.

We made the first project water deliveries to Santa Clara and Alameda counties' water users. We kept the construction on schedule and within plan, while we readied plans for later construction of additional facilities.

The initial facilities of the project were designed and built to a capacity to distribute the 4.23 million acre-feet of water forecasted to be needed 60 years after the project was authorized. The conservation and storage facilities, however, were built to provide only the 2.2 million acre-feet needed by the water service contractors during the first 30 years, i.e., until about 1990. Additional works were scheduled to be built to increase the project yield in an orderly fashion as more water would be needed.

After my time in the governor's office, the schedule which we had adopted for construction of additional works was abandoned. The Peripheral Canal was postponed and after it was revived in my son's administration, it was carried to a referendum and defeated. Authorization for the Dos Rios dam and diversion tunnel project was revoked. It would have provided additional water for the project and, during my administration, was considered the logical next step to be taken to increase safe diversions form the Delta.

The 30 years of float time that we provided in which to plan and construct additional facilities and to devise and put in place alternative works has been frittered away through indecision and inaction.

The drought that was in its fifth year in 1991 has jarred the whole state. The drought has coincided with the actual development of needs that were forecast to occur by 1990. The drought and the growth of demands beyond the capacity of the initial facilities of the State Water Project to satisfy them have revived public interest in a new round of action.

Almost 7 million residents were added to California's population during the 1980s. The state's total population burgeoned to almost 30 million in the 1990 census. In years of normal rainfall, the developed water supplies of the State Water Project, the Central Valley Project and all the other projects that we and our ancestors built, going clear back to the Gold Rush, will not satisfy the needs of farms, industry, the villages, towns, cities and metropolises of 30 million Californians. The growth genie cannot be stuffed back into the canteen. Without additional water development, what we think of as "normal" water years will not meet our needs in the future. It is as though we have entered an era of perpetual drought to be broken only in flood years.

Because of the lapse in our preparations to meet the needs of the next generation of Californians, something must give NOW. A cacophony of suggestions has been made. We must transfer water to cities at agriculture's expense. We must reclaim wastewater for reuse. We must subordinate environmental requirements to consumptive uses. We must desalt the sea. We must belatedly build the Peripheral Canal and new reservoirs. We must adopt conjunctive use of surface and ground water on a statewide scale. We must turn some of the Delta islands into reservoirs, using the levees that were designed to protect the islands' farms from the rivers as circular dams inside of which to store water for later release to irrigators or domestic users elsewhere, or to assist in salvaging the fish runs in the Delta. Ferry icebergs from the Arctic. Tanker fresh water from Canada. Trim back our diversions from the Delta to restore historic environmental values. These and other proposals have been made. Some of the suggestions may be used to serve short-term needs in the emergency. Others will be found to be impractical in this era.

Clearly, a new water program for the state must be worked out. The California economy otherwise will be impoverished, and in the absence of planned action, our vaunted way of life will progressively degrade. We are already very late in undertaking this task. Our float time has been exhausted. A slow desertification is setting in, reducing our world-famous agriculture. The times call stridently for decisions and early action.

This book represents an effort by the Institute that I and a group of friends have endowed to appraise our situation and to offer suggestions by knowledgeable experts of courses of action that may be applicable in this deepening emergency.

CALIFORNIA WATER

Past, Present and Future Issues

Gov. Pete Wilson and former Gov. Pat Brown at a joint legislative session honoring Gov. Brown, March 2, 1992. Photo credit: Water Education Foundation.

BACKGROUND

Water Education Foundation

Water is a curious and unique fluid. Water nourishes agricultural produce and livestock, provides habitat for fish and wildlife and powers turbines which provide energy. Industry uses it for cooling and landscapes need it to survive. We swim in it, ice skate on it and wash with it. And, we drink it.

A family of five uses about one-half to one acre-foot of water per year for all its domestic needs. (An acre-foot of water is enough to cover an acre of land to a depth of one foot, approximately 326,000 gallons.) Additionally, an estimated 25 acre-feet of water are needed to grow food for that family, according to a study done at the University of California, Berkeley.

The California Department of Water Resources estimates the state's net water use in 1985 was 34.2 million acre-feet. This is expected to increase to 36 million acre-feet by the year 2010. California's population is now 30 million; by 2010 it will swell to over 39 million.

California is the nation's leader in agricultural production, with an estimated 9.7 million acres of land producing at least 200 commercial crops, adding $17 billion per year to California's economy.

The Water Education Foundation is a private, nonprofit, nonpartisan organization. Its mission is to develop and implement educational programs leading to a broader understanding of water issues and to resolution of water problems.

In a normal year, California receives nearly 200 million acre-feet of precipitation. About 65 percent is lost to evaporation, transpiration by plants and deep percolation. Of the remaining 75 million acre-feet of statewide runoff, 32 percent flows into rivers and ultimately the ocean; 31 percent (about 80 percent of the state's developed water supply) is used by agriculture; 29 percent is protected under the wild and scenic river system or used for Sacramento-San Joaquin Delta fresh water and fish flow requirements; 2 percent flows into Nevada; and 6 percent is used by cities and industry.

This supply is unpredictable because of changes in the weather—runoff has ranged from as little as 15 million acre-feet in 1976-1977 to more than 135 million acre-feet in 1982-1983. There is about 250 million acre-feet of accessible water in the state's 350 ground water basins. In some basins, water is being used more rapidly than it is being recharged. About 40 percent of California's water supply comes from ground water, but this proportion increases when drought conditions limit available surface water, such as during 1976-1977 and 1987-1992.

About three-quarters of the available water originates north of Sacramento, while three-quarters of the demand occurs in southern California. Precipitation varies from more than 100 inches a year in California's northwestern corner to less than 2 inches in the inland deserts that border Mexico.

Normal water storage in California's major reservoirs is about 28 million acre-feet. But the seasonal distribution of precipitation makes getting the water into the reservoirs tricky. The greatest water needs for agriculture and landscape irrigation occur in the dry summer months. But most rainfall occurs from October through April—flood season.

Many of the state's water supply reservoirs function also as flood control reservoirs, and water managers face a yearly dilemma. Enough storage must be reserved for flood control, should it be needed, but once the need for flood control ends, runoff must be captured in the reservoirs for use in California's long, dry summers.

Central to discussions about California water is the Sacramento-San Joaquin Delta, a 700,000-acre region where the Sacramento and San Joaquin rivers meet. Through the Delta's maze of waterways passes water to satisfy the demands of the Delta itself, the San Francisco Bay and Bay Area, the agricultural lands of the San Joaquin Valley and millions of southern Californians.

These are the physical facts of water in California. The history of the amazing water system of California, the problems confronted and solved over the years, the crucial issues we face today, the controversies and emotions behind the facts, and possible solutions for the future, are discussed in these pages.

California's earliest history was connected to water. Lack of a reliable supply of water at the site of the first Spanish mission in San Diego caused it to fail. The padres moved down the valley to a site on the San Diego River where the mission thrived. Photo credit: California State Library.

A BRIEFING ON CALIFORNIA WATER ISSUES

Betty Brickson and Rita Schmidt Sudman

As the nation's most populous state, California faces many complex and pressing economic, social and environmental problems. Principal among these is the management of the state's limited water supply and how—or if—that supply can be stretched to meet increasing demands. Not only is California's population expected to swell to over 35 million by the turn of the century (with much of this growth occurring in semi-arid central and southern California), but demands for more reliable and higher quality water supplies have come from agricultural, environmental and urban users. Satisfying these competing demands is the challenge that water managers will face into the next century.

If the current drought—now entering its sixth year—has taught us anything, it's that if available supplies are not used more efficiently and/or expanded, California's future may be seen today along the Central Coast, where dry reservoirs, lost jobs, overdrafted ground water basins and water rationing have become commonplace. The environmental toll of prolonged drought has also heightened public demands for increased supplies for instream uses to preserve and enhance fisheries and other wildlife and recreational values. The quality of water is also a major factor, as

Rita Schmidt Sudman is executive director of the Water Education Foundation. Betty Brickson is a consulting writer for the Water Education Foundation.

public concern over and the regulation of contaminants in drinking water supplies increases.

The position of the state Department of Water Resources (DWR) is that with proper management, development and distribution, California has adequate surface and ground water supplies to carry the state well into the next century. By any conventional test, according to DWR, there is plenty of water to go around, but more and more often, competing water users are laying claim to all available supplies. A new interagency task force appointed by Gov. Wilson to evaluate state water policy will make recommendations on programs to meet statewide water needs for the next 20 years. Among the options that the Water Policy Task Force and other state and local water managers are considering are increased urban and agricultural water conservation, wastewater reclamation, water transfers, sea water desalination, conjunctive use of surface and ground water supplies and the possible construction of new storage, pumping and transfer facilities.

Behind the scenes, these options are also being considered by various public interest groups and water agencies that have been trying to reach mutually beneficial solutions to some California water problems. Recently, interest has focused on the work of the Three-Way Water Agreement Process, a coalition of over 60 organizations representing urban, agricultural and environmental water interests that are negotiating to develop a new framework for state water policy. Such consensus-building efforts have been particularly successful in the area of urban water conservation. A historic Memorandum of Understanding, in which over 75 urban water agencies and public interest groups agreed to carry out various water conservation and reuse programs, was signed in December 1991.

The following pages outline the critical issues that will shape California water policy into the next century.

GROWTH

The 1990 census confirmed that California is undergoing the greatest population surge in the state's history. Over the past decade the state experienced a 25 percent growth rate—double the national average—surging 2 to 30 million residents in 1990. Projections indicate that by 2010, over 39 million people will live in the state.

When matching projected demand with existing water supplies and facilities, DWR estimates that in 20 years the state will be at least 1.4 million acre-feet short in drought years. Other estimates by water contractors and municipal water districts place the future statewide deficit at 2.5 million acre-feet in drought years. These estimates apply to surface water supplies and do not account for the state's current 2 million acre-feet in average annual ground water overdraft.

The position of DWR and most local water agencies on accommodating growth is that all reasonable needs should be met and that growth-related decisions are best left to local governments. But others believe that allowing continued development in areas where water supplies are already taxed, especially in drought years, is short-sighted and environmentally unsound. Some argue that providing water induces growth and that growth can be curtailed by restricting water connections and/or raising costs.

Many water managers contend that, in addition to more efficient water use, the state's economic future depends on constructing new water storage and transfer facilities, for example, by adding to the State Water Project (SWP), which has not been completed as planned. But the construction of major projects to enhance the reliability of water supplies for a growing population faces strong political and environmental opposition. The likelihood that local, state and federal agencies can come up with the votes, political will and funding to build such projects is questionable. Increasingly, water agencies are being drawn into the growth management debate as they explore all available options to balance supply with demand.

Water shortage is just one of many problems stemming from rapid population growth. Urban sprawl, traffic congestion, air pollution, environmental degradation and declining services also result. The Wilson administration has taken the position that while growth cannot be stopped, it can be managed. After holding a series of statewide public hearings, the Governor's Growth Management Task Force will make recommendations on how state and local governments can better coordinate long-range planning efforts.

THE BAY-DELTA ENVIRONMENT AND WATER QUALITY

The Sacramento-San Joaquin Delta—a 1,153 square mile region located where California's two greatest rivers converge and flow into San Francisco Bay—is a vital link for the state's water supply as 42 percent of the state's runoff flows through this region. State, federal and local water facilities in the

Delta draw water to farms and cities in the San Francisco Bay Area and central and southern California, providing water to about two-thirds of the state's population. A key to resolving the Delta's very complex and controversial water issues is striking a fair balance among urban, agricultural and environmental water needs.

The State Water Resources Control Board (SWRCB), a powerful five-member board appointed to four-year terms by the governor, periodically revises pollution and salinity standards for Delta water. Under a 1986 state appeals court ruling, the SWRCB has been required to balance all beneficial uses of Bay and Delta waters and, if necessary, modify existing water rights to achieve that balance. Conflicting testimony from competing water interests dominated the last round of water quality hearings. A first draft water quality control plan released in 1988 was withdrawn amid objections from water user groups that it called for unreasonable water conservation goals and unattainable project operation plans. And in September 1991, the Environmental Protection Agency (EPA) rejected key portions of another plan to update Delta water quality standards, citing the lack of sufficient protections for Delta fisheries.

The stakes are high as more than 5,000 holders of water appropriation licenses or permits, including DWR and the U.S. Bureau of Reclamation, face possible changes in water entitlements, primarily losses of water for fish and wildlife uses. Environmentalists and fishery biologists contend that the export of fresh water from the Delta is responsible for declining fish populations, particularly striped bass, Delta smelt, salmon and steelhead, and that the restoration of significant fresh water flows is necessary for the health of the estuary. But water user groups maintain that the estuary is healthy and that increased fresh water flows would be wasted. The board's final decision on water rights and flows is expected in late 1992.

Since voters defeated a controversial proposal to build a Peripheral Canal around the Delta in 1982, DWR has sought to develop smaller projects to improve the Delta. DWR has proceeded with plans to widen key Delta channels, construct major storage facilities south of the Delta and add pumps to increase springtime exports to the south and west. The plans involve engineering and management for flood control, water quality improvement and reducing reverse flow patterns caused by Delta pumps that harm fish and degrade the quality of exported water. Still, the plans have encountered opposition from environmental groups and the EPA, claiming they would further degrade fish and wildlife in the estuary.

Since the Delta is the source of drinking water for 19 million Californians, the quality of this water is very important. Because the Delta was once a swamp, it has rich, organic soils containing compounds which are the building blocks for suspected human carcinogens called trihalomethanes, or THMs. THMs are disinfectant byproducts, formed when chlorine is used to treat drinking water. Possible solutions to the water quality problem might involve costly treatment programs by urban water districts, reducing agricultural drainage into the Delta and its tributaries, diverting water before it travels through the Delta or diverting it in a canal around the Delta. Although the

Peripheral Canal package (Senate Bill #200) was soundly defeated in 1982 in a statewide referendum, there is renewed discussion that an isolated, through-Delta canal might be a solution to Delta water transfer, quality and fishery problems.

In addition to these complex issues, the 1,100 miles of levees that protect Delta islands and channel water through the maze of Delta sloughs are vulnerable to failure from erosion, seepage and earthquakes. If massive failure should occur, experts warn that salt water would flood many Delta islands, forcing Delta water users to rely on stored supplies and seriously disrupting water delivery to central and southern California.

GROUND WATER OVERDRAFT AND CONTAMINATION

California is blessed with large ground water reservoirs which provide about 40 percent of the state's usable water supply in normal years and up to 60 percent in critically dry years. Under normal circumstances, however, Californians use more ground water than is replaced by precipitation, stream seepage or artificial recharge programs. Annual statewide ground water overdraft is estimated to be approximately 2 million acre-feet in a normal year. Overdraft—the long-term decline in ground water storage—can result in lowered water tables and increased energy costs for pumping, dry wells, and in some basins, contamination from the intrusion of sea water or other contaminants. Overdraft can also permanently reduce the storage capacity of some basins due to the compaction of the fine-grained clays which hold the water.

Compaction due to overdraft in the southern San Joaquin Valley, which eased in 1970 when the SWP and federal Central Valley Project (CVP) began delivering surface water for irrigation use, caused 5,200 square miles of the valley floor to subside at least a foot between 1925 and 1977. Studies by the

U.S. Geological Survey indicate that subsidence is presently occurring in some areas of the Sacramento and San Joaquin valleys and in the Antelope Valley in southeastern Kern County. Through construction of ground water recharge projects such as the Kern Water Bank in Kern County, DWR and local water agencies are working to replenish underground aquifers. But the success of these and other recharge projects may depend on the unresolved question of increasing surface water exports from the Sacramento-San Joaquin Delta.

Perhaps a more serious and immediate threat to potable water supplies is the contamination of major ground water basins, particularly in the San Gabriel and San Fernando valleys, from landfills, leaked toxics and solvents. According to DWR, all of the state's ground water basins are contaminated to some degree, but the contamination is usually concentrated in small sections of the basins. The huge cost, complexity and time required to clean up contaminated basins have forced some communities to abandon their wells and rely on imported surface water supplies.   The issues of ground water quantity and quality are intertwined, for when underground aquifers are contaminated, usable supply is reduced. When some coastal aquifers are overdrafted, sea water intrudes and quality declines. In California, ground water pumping is regulated only in adjudicated basins, in special management districts or where the SWRCB has enjoined withdrawals to protect water quality. Some local efforts have been very effective in recharging and cleaning up ground water basins. But California and Texas remain the only western states with no statewide ground water regulation.

WATER CONSERVATION AND MARKETING

Water conservation is an important means of stretching the developed supply, but assessments of how far conservation measures can take the state toward solving future water supply problems vary widely. Conservation programs pulled many communities through recent drought-induced shortages, but using conservation to reduce long-term water demand is a relatively new idea. Water conservation as an ongoing practice in normal years can make society less able to cope in future dry years because the water savings are already incorporated into the system.

Work groups that emerged from the SWRCB's Bay-Delta Proceedings have reached consensus in the area of urban water conservation, culminating in the signing of a Memorandum of Understanding in late 1991. The more than 75 water agencies and public interest groups that signed the MOU agree to implement water conservation programs through Best Management Practices (BMPs). These programs include the installation of water-saving plumbing fixtures in all new construction, water metering, price and/or financial incentives, landscape water surveys, gray water reuse, water audits and public information programs.

However, since agriculture uses about 80 percent of the state's developed water (30 percent of the state's total annual runoff), critics say that urban conservation measures are merely a drop in the bucket compared to agriculture's ability to save water. Some environmentalists and economists say a relatively modest reduction in agricultural water use in California, about 10 percent, could free up enough water, in theory, to permit decades of population growth.

Farmers contend that most of their water is reused within the system (water drained from one field is used to irrigate another) if it does not evaporate, drain to a saline sink or into ground water aquifers. Since the 1980s, irrigated agriculture's water consumption has remained relatively stable at around 9 million irrigated acres, while per-acre production has increased with improved techniques. In the meantime, the urban sector's water needs have passed expectations. This urban growth, especially during a series of drought years, has intensified an interest in marketing agricultural water to the urban sector.

Water marketing, or transfers—the general idea of exchanging, leasing or selling water from one user to another—has been relatively slow to gain acceptance in California compared to other western states. Concerns about the fate of local communities and agriculture-related industries if farmers sell their water and quit farming, and fears of distant domination over local resources have kept agriculture from jumping at the high price urban water users could pay for farm water.

During the past five drought years, however, individual water agencies have arranged many successful short-term transfers. The state became a water broker in 1991 through creation of the Drought Water Bank. Through the bank, the state bought mostly surplus surface water from agricultural users and sold it to critically water-short urban, agricultural and environmental users. 1991 also brought a controversial two-year bill which, if enacted, would free up the California water market by enabling individual water users and buyers to negotiate a trade without the consent of the local water district. The bill, authored by Assemblymember Richard Katz (D-Sepulveda) has divided agricultural and urban water districts, which for years were politically aligned.

Environmentalists are divided on the issue of water marketing. While trades are favored as a partial solution to meeting increasing urban demands without building new water projects, some water transfers have raised serious concerns that the temperature and flow fluctuations caused by the releases are harmful to fish and wildlife, particularly salmon eggs and fry. While transfers have eased the hardships of the current drought, they are not seen as a cure-all for California's water problems, for without the ability to physically transfer water from seller to buyer, a transfer isn't possible.

AGRICULTURAL DRAINAGE

In 1983, the discovery of death and deformity among young waterfowl at the Kesterson National Wildlife Refuge—a San Joaquin Valley wetlands area fed by agricultural drainage water—alerted people to the dangers of toxic concentrations of trace elements in the environment. Decades of surface irrigation in the San Joaquin Valley has led to the leaching of selenium, a naturally occurring trace element which is harmful in high concentrations, from soils in parts of the south and west sides of the valley into the shallow ground water basins.

Subsurface drainage systems are commonly used throughout the Imperial, Coachella and San Joaquin valleys to drain excess or saline water from the root zone, where dense soils prevent water from percolating into the subsurface at the same rate it is applied to the land. The discharge of this drainage water, tainted with high concentrations of salts and, in places, selenium, arsenic, boron and other trace elements, is a major concern. In addition to Kesterson, some wetlands, evaporation ponds and channels in the

Tulare Basin and Los Banos area have been found to have selenium levels in excess of those deemed safe by the EPA and SWRCB.

A September 1990 report by the San Joaquin Valley Drainage Program forecasts that if current irrigation practices continue, salt- and trace element-tainted, shallow ground water levels will adversely affect 40 percent of the west side of the valley's irrigable farmland, threatening a major part of the valley's $7 billion a year agricultural industry. The report recommends the retirement of approximately 75,000 acres of farmland deemed too difficult to drain. To reduce the volume of drainage water, the report recommends maximum possible on-farm water conservation and the reuse of drainage water by a variety of salt-tolerant plants. The remaining, highly concentrated drainage water would be discharged into evaporation ponds, redesigned to discourage wildlife use.

ALLOCATION OF WATER FOR FISH AND WILDLIFE

Along with providing more reliable supplies for urban and agricultural users, a critical challenge for the 1990s will be providing more water for fish and wildlife uses. A 1990 Field Institute poll of Californians' views on water indicated that in times of water shortages, the public ranked environmental protection highest in importance as an essential use of water over other uses, including agriculture or to accommodate population growth. "State residents appear to be adamant about not accepting environmental degradation as a consequence of water shortage unless there is no practical alternative," the poll states.

This rise in public support for environmental preservation, combined with powerful lobbying by environmental groups and the passage of strict state and federal laws protecting endangered species and plant and wildlife habitat, have effectively blocked most conventional water development over the past two decades. Recent court decisions restricting the amount of water the Los Angeles Department of Water and Power can divert from tributaries feeding Mono Lake point to the increased power of environmental groups to challenge longstanding water rights through legal claims based on the Public Trust Doctrine. The doctrine, which holds that certain natural resources are the property of all, was expanded in a 1983 decision by the state Supreme Court to protect natural areas, fish and wildlife in addition to navigation and commerce.

Critics contend the doctrine threatens to undermine state water law and water supplies to cities and farms by allowing environmental claims on all vested water rights. But environmentalists maintain that mitigation is necessary for past management practices that have placed agricultural, industrial and urban water needs above those of fish and wildlife, bringing many species to the brink of extinction. The SWRCB's Bay-Delta Proceedings have become the focus of the state debate over giving higher priority to instream water uses. Nationally, bills sponsored by New Jersey Sen. Bill Bradley and California Rep. George Miller, are pending in Congress, which would overhaul the way water is allocated through the CVP to provide more water for environmental uses.

The new power of environmental interests—which has grown to equal that of urban and agricultural water interests—is perhaps most evident in the stated goals of the Three-Way Water Agreement Process. The goals of this ad hoc group, a coalition of urban, agricultural and environmental water user representatives who are negotiating to help resolve California's water problems, include the possible formation of an Environmental Water Authority. This new entity could enter into contracts with state and federal water project operators to secure water for wildlife use, just as urban and agricultural users do.

Large cattle ranches were common during the Mexican period in California. This early scale of farming and ranching set the style for later day farming operations. When the federal government built water projects for irrigation and flood control in the Central Valley, it required the farmers to agree to acre limitations in order to receive subsidized water. Arguments over federal subsidies to assist agriculture continue today. Photo credit: California State Library.

STATE WATER PLANNING: FINDING COMMON GROUND

David N. Kennedy and Stanley M. Barnes

In the long history of California water development, the year 1959 was of particular significance. First, in 1959 the California Water Plan was approved by the Legislature. It was intended to be the guide for orderly and coordinated control, protection, conservation, development and utilization of the water resources of the state. Second, the Burns-Porter Act passed the Legislature that same year. It was designed to move statewide water management from planning to construction. Both acts faced difficult battles in the Legislature and both were successful, in large part due to the extraordinary efforts of then Gov. Edmund G. "Pat" Brown.

Debate over how to manage the state's water resources, by whom and under what restraints, have long been topics for vigorous discussion in California. The debate was not quieted with the enactment of either of the 1959 pieces of legislation. There were strong opponents as well as proponents to both proposals. Given the current geographic split on water issues in California, it is interesting to look back at the 1959 legislative votes. The "no" votes in the Senate on Burns-Porter were all from northern

David N. Kennedy was appointed director of the California Department of Water Resources in 1983. Before his appointment as director, he was assistant general manager of Metropolitan Water District of Southern California.
Stanley M. Barnes is a consulting engineer and a member of the California Water Commission.

California. They were generally from the Delta, north of the Delta and mountain counties as far south as Mariposa. Interestingly, senators from the Bay Area and the counties of Solano, Sacramento and Butte voted in favor of the bill.

Voting in the Assembly was more mixed. There were "no" votes from south of the Tehachapis and many more from the San Francisco and Monterey bay areas, in addition to the areas that voted "no" in the Senate. The Burns-Porter Act passed the Senate by a vote of 25 to 12 and the Assembly by a vote of 50 to 30. While both the California Water Plan and the Burns-Porter Act are milestones in California's long-standing efforts to provide orderly development of the state's water supplies, it is clear from the Burns-Porter vote tallies that the matter was highly controversial, touching on a number of complex issues in water resource management. Many of these issues are not resolved today. Indeed, controversies surrounding most of the issues have become even more volatile and the arena in which these controversies are played out is even more complex.

STATE WATER PROJECT: AN HISTORICAL PERSPECTIVE

The Burns-Porter Act was ratified by the voters in November 1960 in a close election. A large percentage of northern Californians voted against the measure. However, greater percentages of southern Californians voted in support of the measure and it was approved by a margin of 150,000 votes. The act authorized a bond issue of $1.75 billion to assist in statewide water development. It provided funding for construction of some facilities needed immediately and a plan to progressively implement additional stages of the system as they were needed.

The act listed the specific facilities to be constructed as part of the state water resources development system. These facilities included:

1. Oroville Dam and Reservoir, afterbay facilities, pumping-generating plants, fish hatchery and related facilities, and five upstream dams and reservoirs;

2. North Bay Aqueduct from the Delta to Solano, Napa and Marin counties;

3. Delta levees, control structures, channel improvements and appurtenant facilities for water conservation, water supply, transfer of water across the Delta, flood and salinity control and related functions;

4. South Bay Aqueduct from the Delta to Alameda and Santa Clara counties;

5. San Luis Dam and Reservoir, pumping-generating plant, San Luis Canal and facilities for offstream storage and conveyance of unregulated surplus water pumped from the Delta, a federal-state joint use project;

6. Edmund G. "Pat" Brown California Aqueduct, from the Delta to southern California;

7. Facilities for the removal of drainage water from the San Joaquin Valley;

8. Facilities for the generation and transmission of electrical energy;

9. Water development facilities for local areas.

The Legislature did not identify individual local projects for funding, but set aside $130 million for loans and grants to assist local agencies in developing water supply and recreational facilities.

After the Burns-Porter Act was adopted, water suppliers contracted for large amounts of water in anticipation of urban expansion and agricultural growth. The State Water Project (SWP) contracted to ultimately deliver over 4 million acre-feet of water per year. Water suppliers believed that not only would the demand increase, but that there was an adequate supply of usable water within the state to meet those needs. As California continued to grow and the need for water increased, it was understood that additions to the State Water Project would be planned and constructed to meet those needs.

In 1982, some 20 years later, in an unusual referendum of a bill that passed the Legislature in 1980, the people of California voted overwhelmingly against proceeding with construction of storage and water transfer facilities to complete the State Water

Project. The centerpiece of the legislation was the Peripheral Canal, but the "package" included other facilities and various environmental protection measures. At times, it seemed that everyone involved had a different perception of what was included in the package. By a majority of 90 percent, 35 northern California counties voted against the proposition.

Proponents of the canal argued that it was needed to save the Sacramento-San Joaquin River Delta from further degradation, to ensure reliable delivery of water south of the Delta and to ease the pressure on overdrafted ground water basins in the San Joaquin Valley. Opponents of the initiative were sometimes described as the "unholy alliance." Opponents in the San Francisco Bay Area and northern California argued that the cost of such a project was prohibitive, that more water would fuel the explosive growth in southern California at the expense of natural resources in the North, that northern California needed water for its own growth, and that there were less costly, more environmentally sound solutions to the water problems facing the state. Some of the state water contractors opposed the initiative because they believed the environmental guarantees would impose severe restrictions that would seriously reduce the additional project yield created by the Peripheral Canal.

The droughts of 1976-1977 and 1987-1991 and the Peripheral Canal referendum in 1982 again brought water to the forefront of media attention. Issues previously of interest mainly to policy-makers, water officials and agricultural interests have become topics of conversation for much of the populace. Water supply and its impact on the economy, on the environment and on personal well-being are now matters on which people are eager to voice an opinion. In some ways, new state and federal laws dealing with protection of environmental resources have made resolution of water issues even more difficult than in earlier years.

EVOLVING ENVIRONMENTAL PROTECTION STATUTES

Growing concern about the impacts of toxics and hazardous substances is reflected in public health concerns over the purity of drinking water sources. There is also a growing concern about the disappearance of wetland, riparian and stream habitat and protection of threatened and endangered species. This public concern has been reflected in a proliferation of state and federal laws aimed at improving water quality and protecting environmental values. The ever-expanding laws have led to development of an elaborate regulatory scheme on both the federal and state levels to administer these laws.

Although there is a continuing need for more secure high quality water supplies to meet agricultural and urban uses, there is heated disagreement on how best to meet these needs. One of the most significant factors in this debate is the concern over the environmental impacts of not only proposed water supply facilities, but existing ones.

While there were discussions about environmental impacts of the Burns-Porter Act on the Delta in the 1950s, there is a much greater public awareness of the issues today. With the proliferation of environmental legislation in the 1970s and toxics and hazardous waste laws in the 1980s, environmental concerns have become part of the mainstream decision-making process for water suppliers. The National Environmental Policy Act and the California Environmental Quality Act require study of the environmental impacts of federal and state projects early in their planning process. Both laws require public access to information, an opportunity for public comment and that concerns be addressed by the decision-making agency.

With modern technology, it is now possible to detect and quantify exceedingly minute concentrations of many exotic chemicals which, in larger concentrations, are known to cause cancer and other serious health problems. Unfortunately, the realistic health hazard of toxic chemicals in such minute concentrations is very difficult to determine and, in most cases, has not been determined. It is also unfortunate that, in such small concentrations, removal of the substances to nondetectable levels is exceedingly difficult and costly. Nevertheless, until such health hazards are reliably determined to exist or not exist, there will be continued public concern and therefore continued enforcement of stringent standards by the federal and state regulatory agencies.

Other laws allow for citizen enforcement of environmental standards. For example, the federal Clean Water Act has citizen suit provisions allowing an individual dissatisfied with government enforcement of provisions of the act to pursue an alleged polluter under specified procedures. Although not used extensively, this provision has been used in the past and is currently available for use. The California Safe Drinking Water and Toxics Enforcement Act (Proposition 65) also allows citizen suits if a person is dissatisfied with government enforcement. The Proposition 65 citizen suit provisions allow an individual successful in prosecuting a violator to keep a portion of the damages for which the violator is found liable.

Use of the courts for remedies to long-standing water debates is becoming more frequent. In 1979, the National Audubon Society and others sued the Los Angeles Department of Water and Power (LADWP), alleging that LADWP's diversions violated California's public trust doctrine. Although the case has a complicated procedural history, the public trust issue was eventually presented to the California Supreme Court. In 1983, the court held that the public trust doctrine applies to all existing water diversion rights that may affect navigable waterways. The court found that the state has an affirmative duty to consider public trust values in issuing water rights permits and licenses and it has a continuing duty of supervision and reconsideration of existing water rights to protect trust values whenever feasible. The court made it clear that the public trust values were to be weighed against other beneficial uses of water. Finally, the court held that the State Water Resources Control Board and the judiciary have concurrent original jurisdiction over public trust issues.

Another series of cases brought by environmental and fishing organizations against LADWP focused on the stream flows and fishery resources of the four streams tributary to Mono Lake. In January 1989, the Third District Court of Appeal ruled that the State Water Resources Control Board must modify two of Los Angeles's long-standing water licenses to require fish-sustaining flows in the four tributaries. The California Supreme Court refused to hear Los Angeles's appeal. The State Water Resources Control Board is currently reviewing the license and expects to make its decision in December 1992. In the interim, El Dorado Superior Court Judge Terrence Finney issued an order requiring that between 58,000 and 74,000 acre-feet of water be released into the tributaries according to a specified schedule.

Over 10 years of litigation has now been waged over the water in the Mono Basin. The environmentalists have used the common law doctrine of public trust, the California Fish and Game Code and the federal Clean Air Act to limit Los Angeles's diversions from the basin. When the Third District Court of Appeal ruled in March 1990 that Los Angeles must release water immediately to maintain fish in the four tributaries, the court also awarded Los Angeles's opponents' attorneys fees. The court ordered not only that Los Angeles, et al. pay Cal Trout and others their attorneys' fees for work already done, but also that Los Angeles and the others pay the environmentalists' attorney fees in the future if further actions are required to force compliance with the Fish and Game Code.

Most environmental and toxics laws establish a state or federal agency to administer and enforce the requirements of the laws. Many proposed water projects fall under the regulation of the U.S. Crops of Engineers and the Environmental Protection Agency (EPA). These agencies jointly administer the provisions of the Clean Water Act concerning dredge and fill material in the waters of the United States (Section 404). Until recently, the Corps of Engineers administered this provision almost entirely. Recently, EPA has become much more active in the granting or denial of these permits. EPA holds veto authority over the Corps' ability to grant a 404 permit. EPA's administrative charge is to study, protect and advise the administration on environmental issues and concerns. Consequently, EPA's review of a project has a different focus than that of the Corps.

It is difficult to propose any project affecting water without falling under the Section 404 jurisdiction. The phrase "waters of the United States" has been interpreted so broadly that most waterways and wetlands within the state are covered. This means as a practical matter that the federal government, through EPA, has veto power over most water projects. Agencies sponsoring new projects must therefore deal with EPA's concerns in the long and torturous process of moving a project forward.

The complex regulatory processes, both federal and state, that have evolved in recent years are so new that few agencies have actually received approval for any new projects. It is clear, though, that the agency sponsoring a project must acknowledge the inherent complexities of water issues, including past battles, look to the factual, political and regulatory realities, and sculpt a problem-solving approach that acknowledges these facts. With the wealth of resource protection laws, the increase in public participation on both an organized group level and an individual one, as well as the ever-increasing vigilance of regulatory agencies and the national and local media, the most practical method of project development today appears to be a consensus-building process where issues are addressed in a series of individual, but coordinated problem-solving steps.

One important aspect of environmental concern that has received special attention is the restoration and rehabilitation of fisheries resources that were degraded by earlier water projects and by other human activities. As an example, a group representing widely divergent interests concerned about the upper Sacramento River worked for three years to develop recommendations for measures aimed at halting the decline of stream and riparian habitat quality and quantity. Former state Sen. Jim Nielsen sponsored Senate Bill 1086 to formally establish the Upper Sacramento River Advisory Council and direct it to study the river from Verona upstream to Keswick Dam. Representatives of federal, state and local agencies, environmentalists, sport and commercial fishing organizations and others concerned about the upper Sacramento resources met for three years to study the area, discuss their sometimes diverse concerns and analyze potential solutions.

The council developed a 23-point, 10-year plan aimed at halting the decline of the fishery and riparian environment. The recommendations included building more fish ladders and screens, replacing spawning gravel and making other habitat improvements in the river channel, as well as the riparian areas. The advisory council and others are currently seeking federal legislative authorization and appropriations to help implement the 10-year plan. State and local funds will also be needed. The negotiation process that led to this proposed program is an example of how widely divergent interests can work together and find common ground when they are willing to approach the issues with patience and an open mind.

THE FUTURE

Knowing California's history of disputes over water and with the increasing demand and continued stress upon existing water supply systems, debates over issues of water supply will no doubt continue for many years. Areas throughout the state are facing problems of limited water supplies, overdrafted ground water basins, agricultural drainage problems, disappearing wetlands, decreasing fish and wildlife populations and increasing concerns over drinking water purity.

The most significant water issue for Californians in the next few years will be development of additional facilities for the State Water Project. The existing facilities are nearing full utilization and long-standing Delta transfer problems must be dealt with in order to meet the present water needs within the SWP service area from the San Francisco Bay Area to San Diego. It will be imperative that the state administration proceed with a development program for Delta facilities and for storage at the Kern Water Bank and Los Banos Grandes Reservoir.

There will no doubt be continued vigorous discussion among all interests about how to proceed with additional facilities. While there is strong support for these facilities in the abstract, some people argue that nothing should be done until new Bay-Delta water quality standards are in place. Others propose that a comprehensive package of facilities and measures be fashioned to address all of the major problems in some type of overall accommodation.

It is our view, based on the state's difficult experience with water issues in recent years and the growing regulatory presence of the federal government in water issues, that the most promising approach is to continue with step-by-step activities based on negotiation and accommodation among the various interests. While this can be slow and frustrating, one of the realities of broad public support for environmental protection is that state and federal legislators are unlikely to grant exemptions form environmental statues. This means that all water projects, no matter how widespread their public support, must pick their way through the complex, detailed regulatory schemes that have been established. In the regulatory framework there is no room for broad political accommodations such as were so effectively fashioned by Gov. Pat Brown. Legislators have set forth the environmental policies and then turned over to regulators the responsibility for dealing with specific projects. We therefore see little practical alternative to a step-by-step process.

Nevertheless, even though the process today is exceedingly complex, we believe progress has been made in recent years and can continue in the future. Ultimately, there must be balanced programs, respecting the water needs of both people and the environment: reliable water supplies and protection of environmental resources must be worked out in a spirit of accommodation among all interests. The people of California will demand no less.

ONE STATE, THEN AND NOW

Ronald B. Robie

"One State" was the theme of the campaign in 1960 in support of the $1.75 billion bond issue to construct the State Water Project (SWP). This slogan appeared on bumper stickers, posters and in advertisements in favor of Proposition 1 that year.

However, the slogan was more than mere campaign rhetoric. When the California Legislature passed the Burns-Porter Act in 1959 and placed the bonds on the ballot, the objective was a water program for the entire state, not just the thirsty areas of California which would receive water from the SWP.

Originally, the SWP was designed not only to serve southern California and the southern part of the San Joaquin Valley, but several northern California counties as well, including those in the San Francisco Bay Area. Of the latter, Marin County opted out, but the project as it went forward included substantial deliveries to Alameda and Santa Clara counties. Northern California legislators made additional efforts to ensure that areas north of the Delta also benefitted from the project. The Burns-Porter Act included a special provision that $120 million in bond proceeds would be utilized to give grants and loans to local public agencies in the areas of origin (primarily in northern California) for water supply and fish and wildlife enhancement projects. The state's unique "area of origin" and "watershed protection" statutes were designed

---

Ronald B. Robie is former director of the California Department of Water Resources. He is now a Sacramento Superior Court judge.

to make certain that these areas where water originated would have sufficient water to meet their needs even as exports took place. Finally, bonds were set aside to build new facilities to add to the water supply as exports increased.

It was pounded home in every address by the late Assemblyman Carley V. Porter, co-author of the Burns-Porter Act which authorized the project, that only "surplus" waters were to be exported from the Delta.

Porter, Gov. Edmund G. "Pat" Brown and other sponsors of the Burns-Porter Act recognized that Californians could not be expected to approve the largest bond issue ever placed before a state's voters unless the project served the entire state.

In 1960, when Proposition 1 was narrowly approved, major components of the federal Central Valley Project (CVP) were already in place but its diversions from the Sacramento-San Joaquin Delta were not great. Many feared a tremendous impact of the combined state and federal projects on the water quality of the Delta (and some San Francisco Bay Area interests opposed Proposition 1) but the impact was speculative. In many ways, it was not until the environmental revolution of the 1970s that northern California fears focused most strongly on the environmental impacts of diversions.

At the time it enacted the Burns-Porter Act, the Legislature could not have not recognized the full extent of the relationship between Delta water diversions and water quality. It was not until 1967 that the Legislature acted to combine the administration of water quality and water rights with the establishment of the State Water Resources Control Board. Until then, water rights for the projects did not deal effectively with water quality impacts of diversions. The State Board recognized the importance of protecting the water quality of the Delta as a condition of water export when it issued its Decision 1379 in 1971. This decision made clear that the *Delta came first*, before exports. Of course, protection of the water quality of the Delta was not just for municipal and agricultural uses, but those environmental needs of fish, wildlife and recreation, as well.

Shortly thereafter, in 1972, the federal government established a national water quality control program by enactment by Congress of what is now known as the "Clean Water Act," which complemented the state emphasis.

Many continuing northern California fears over water exports were grounded on the fact that the major exporter, the federal government, for years had denied both any congressional requirement on the CVP to protect Delta water quality and any authority of the state through water rights to control operations of the CVP. During the 1977 drought, the federal project thumbed its nose at tough state environmental standards and the SWP had to release water to make up for the lack of federal water quality releases.

Previously, the federal government objected to the State Board's Decision 1379 (and its successor, Decision 1485). It was not until 1978, in *California* v. *United States*, 438 U.S. 645, that the U.S. Supreme Court ruled that the federal CVP must comply with state water rights laws in its operation unless there is a clear congressional directive to the contrary. However, even with this decision, resistance to accepting the state's authority continued, undermining legislative efforts to expand the SWP. In 1986, the federal government finally executed the Coordinated Operation Agreement (COA) for the state and federal projects.

The tremendous impact of the state and federal water projects on the Delta, and especially its fisheries, is now better recognized but physical solutions to the impacts are still far from fully understood, as it is a complex ecosystem.

Another barrier to consensus in the past was that the authority of the State Board to provide a high level of protection to the Delta as a condition of export was challenged by many water users who objected to the environmental protections provided in Decisions 1379 and 1485.

The board's clear authority was not approved by the courts until the decision in *United States* v. *State Water Resources Control Board*, (1986) 182 Cal. App. 3d. 82. The board's authority was further defined in 1983 when the California Supreme Court, in *National Audubon Society* v. *Superior Court*, 33 Cal. 3d. 419, held that the public trust doctrine attached to the navigable waters of the state, including the Delta. This landmark decision gave significant new authority to the state to protect its water resources. The decision, of course, depends on the appointees to the State Water Resources Control Board recognizing its requirements and implementing it fully.

Unfortunately, when the administration of Gov. Edmund G. Brown Jr. presented the Legislature with a program of greater Delta protection together with additional water supply facilities for the SWP, the clear legal authority of the state to protect the Delta and to bind the federal government had not been established.

A persuasive objection to both legislative packages, Senate Bill 346 (which failed) and Senate Bill 200 (which was adopted by the Legislature in 1980 but repealed by the people in a referendum in 1982), was the fear of people in northern California and the Delta that the bills' guarantees were not strong enough, nor permanent. This was understandable in view of the time it took to validate the principle of Delta protection in the courts in the face of longstanding opposition of many state and federal water contractors, primarily agricultural, to the concept of full Delta protection. Some major agricultural water contractors supported the referendum on Senate Bill 200 because it provided too much Delta protection.

Originally, the SWP was to have been making its maximum deliveries in 1990. Fortunately, early projections of water needs were off base and project use developed more slowly. Now, in the 1990s, the SWP is short of its committed supplies. On the other hand, the federal CVP was overbuilt and still has supplies uncommitted. The water policies of the Reagan administration, together with massive federal budget deficits, have all but shut off the spigot on new federal water project construction. For example, Auburn Dam is now looked upon as a flood control facility, not as a water supply project.

In the last 15 years or so, major changes have taken place in the state's approach to water management. In 1975, a water management policy was adopted for DWR which emphasized the conservation of water and the maximum use of existing supplies before new supplies are provided. Our "Save Water" motto was more than a slogan—it drove the activities of the department. The Office of Water Conservation was established by DWR in 1979 and the State Board set up the Office of Water Recycling.

Both municipal and agricultural water agencies throughout the state are doing far more in the area of water conservation, much of which has been mandated by the Legislature, than was done a decade ago. The State Board and DWR have also exercised their authority to prevent the waste of water under Article X, Section 2 of the California Constitution and this power has been upheld by the courts in *Imperial Irrigation District v. State Water Resources Control Board* (1986) Cal. App. 3d. 1160.

The water management policy which was adopted by both DWR and the State Board can guide the search for consensus in this new era today. It provides:

1. Water resources already developed shall be used to the maximum extent before new sources are developed.

2. Water quality objectives, beneficial uses and water quality control plans and policies adopted by the State Water Resources Control Board and the Regional Water Quality Control Boards shall be an integral part of the basis for water resources management.

3. Conjunctive use of surface and ground water supplies and storage capacity shall be used to obtain the greatest practical yield and still protect water quality.

4. Water development plans shall achieve maximum practicable conservation and efficient use of the water for the state.

5. Water shall be reclaimed and reused to the maximum extent feasible.

6. Point sources and nonpoint sources of pollution shall be controlled to protect adopted beneficial uses of water.

7. Instream beneficial uses shall be maintained and, when practical, restored and enhanced.

8. Methods of preventing property damage or loss of life due to floods must consider flood pain zoning, flood proofing, flood warning systems and similar nonstructural measures, as well as construction of facilities such as dams, reservoirs and levees.

9. Energy considerations shall be made an integral part of the water resources planning process (*DWR Bulletin 4*, January 1982).

Implementation of these policies can provide the framework for the Legislature and the governor to evaluate additional needs of the SWP. While at the time of their formulation these polices were criticized by many water developers, they have stood the test of time.

Today, we now have a state committed to conservation and reuse and clear legal authority to protect areas of origin. Many reasons for regional distrust have been eliminated. The time to build consensus is now.

The solution to the state's water problems must:

1. Provide benefits to the entire state. We are still "one state." The SWP met the crisis needs of northern California in the 1977 drought. A pipeline was built across the Richmond-San Rafael Bridge to the same Marin County that rejected the SWP at the outset. Water was delivered to the city of San Francisco (and again in 1990) and emergency supplies were delivered to Alameda and Contra Costa counties.

The fish and wildlife needs of the Delta and northern California are needs of the entire state. These environmental resources belong to all the people. They are part of every citizen's heritage.

2. The solution must be adopted by the Legislature. While additions to the SWP might legally be added by administrative action, no solution will be successful unless it is politically acceptable to the entire state. But mere legislative approval will not assure this success. We have the lesson of Senate Bill 200 to demonstrate this. The solution must be jointly developed by the

administration and the Legislature. The task is formidable. We have years of regional distrust to overcome.

3. The solution must recognize the policies above, and most importantly must be true to the commitment of 1960—"only waters surplus to the needs of the north will be exported."

The water needs of the state can be met by nothing less than a program which recognizes that we are still "One State."

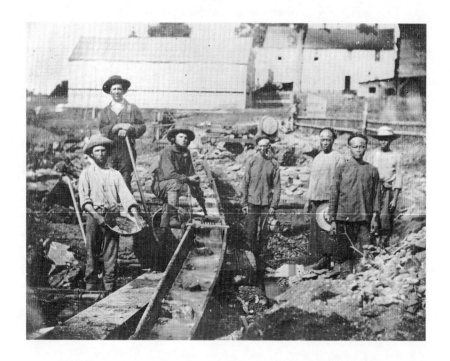

The rivers of California provided the gold which attracted people from all over the world, including these Chinese laborers who called California the "Gold Mountain." Photo credit: California State Library.

ACHIEVING CONSENSUS ON WATER POLICY IN CALIFORNIA

John P. Fraser

INTRODUCTION

California's liquid gold has been and continues to be its water resources. Instrumental to the prosperity of the state, water and its development have afforded California a world-class economy and have made it among the most desirable places to live.

Just as California's water has been its greatest asset, the years of policy gridlock over water plans at the state and federal levels, intense population growth and five years of drought have made water one of the most important issues of the day. It is the culmination of these circumstances and others that have led to the most serious water situation California has ever faced. Examination of some of the most pressing issues indicates that the reliability of our water supply can no longer be taken for granted and is, in fact, at risk.

The good news is that according to a 1990 Field Institute public opinion poll, commissioned by the Association of California Water Agencies (ACWA), Californians are concerned

Since 1970, John P. Fraser has held the position of executive director/general counsel for the Association of California Water Agencies (ACWA). Formed in 1910 under the name of the Irrigation Districts Association, ACWA represents approximately 400 California public water agencies, responsible for over 90 percent of all water delivered in California.

about water. Californians ranked an adequate water supply to meet the state's needs as one of the most critical problems facing the state in the next decade, second only to drugs.

In essence, the public has arrived at a consensus with respect to the importance of water as an issue. The drought has done much to heighten the urgency of California's water problems. The question now is whether our elected and appointed officials will provide the direction that will bring about resolution of the state's ongoing water crisis. One would hope that our elected officials will react to this public concern in much the way former Sen. Everett Dirkson of Illinois did when he said, "When I begin to feel the heat, I begin to see the light."

COMPLEX ISSUES CLOUD CONSENSUS

Drought

Drought, perhaps more than any other single issue, has catapulted water to the forefront of public concern—a place it has not occupied for more than two decades.

While the state's economy has shown some resiliency to the drought thus far, a sixth year of drought is daunting. It is clear that another dry year would have potentially devastating effects: increased dependence on ground water, already heavily overdrafted in some areas; water quality degradation; diminished agricultural production and related losses to theeconomy; mandatory and voluntary water rationing in urban areas; significant impacts on fish and wildlife; and severe damage to forests and other resources.

Growth and Urban Water Shortages

New state census figures indicate that California must now meet the water supply needs of 32 million residents and anticipate the needs of nearly 800,000 new Californians each year. It is clear that California's water supply system has not kept pace with its burgeoning population. The state Department of Water Resources (DWR) estimates that without construction of additional facilities, by 2010 the State Water Project (SWP), the major statewide water system for urban areas, will be unable to meet the needs of the people it serves in seven out of 10 years. In the meantime, the reliability of the state's water system has emerged as a chief concern in the industrial sector. Leading economists agree that the lack of reliable water supplies is one factor undermining the state's business climate.

Agricultural Water Shortages

The drought and growing demands on the state's available water have left agricultural water users facing shortages in surface water supplies. To cope with the reductions, agricultural users rely more heavily on ground water. This practice is not without long-term consequences, however.

The overdrafting of ground water basins in the San Joaquin Valley that began in the early 1970s has been exacerbated by the increased ground water pumping in response to both the 1976-1977 drought and the current dry cycle. The heavy shift to ground water in 1991 in the wake of cuts in surface supplies and the high cost of Gov. Wilson's water bank has further accelerated the problem in the valley, where ground water tables already were being overdrawn to the tune of 2 million acre-feet annually in normal years. Overdraft problems in not only the San Joaquin Valley but also in the Salinas Valley and along the central coast promise to lead to poorer water quality and an increased potential for land subsidence.

Additionally, many agricultural areas face new challenges posed by urban development. Central Valley cities such as Modesto and Fresno are among the fastest-growing areas in the state, adding to the demand already placed on stressed surface and ground water supplies.

Diminishing Supplies

Add to the scenario of drought and growth the fact that California will suffer a net reduction in its available water supply. Arizona continues to take more of its share from the Colorado

River, while at the same time no new "buckets" or storage facilities have been added to our water supply system.

Legal curbs on supplies imported by the city of Los Angeles, increased water quality regulations for drinking water, expected new water quality standards in the Sacramento-San Joaquin Delta and the growing emphasis on the needs of fisheries and endangered species are among factors placing demands on current supplies. As DWR Director David N. Kennedy noted early in 1991, nearly every acre-foot of developed water is now allocated for some specific use. No longer is it possible to increase allocations to any one user, including the environment, without taking some away from others.

Kennedy also has noted that virtually every water development—existing or proposed—now faces legal challenges in one arena or another. Given these dynamics, one can only conclude that water shortages will become a way of life in California unless steps are taken now to overcome our water supply deficiencies.

CONSERVATION AND WATER MANAGEMENT

Few will dispute the need to use all natural resources as efficiently as possible, especially water. Conservation should be an ethic adopted by citizens, agriculture and industry alike, and the public responded effectively to calls to conserve in 1991.

Nonetheless, studies have shown the potential for conservation is finite. As conservation practices become ingrained, the flexibility to respond to further cuts in supply is greatly diminished. Once water-saving practices are in place, further savings on demand can become nearly impossible to achieve. As a matter of policy, overreliance on conservation practices instead of an integrated, long-term water supply mix is setting the state on a course toward chronic future water shortages—drought or not.

Sacramento-San Joaquin Delta

The Sacramento-San Joaquin Delta is perhaps the most critical area in the state with respect to water. The Delta, source of drinking water for 20 million Californians and irrigation water for nearly 2 million acres of farmland, is in serious trouble. Earthquake vulnerability, degrading water quality and the downward slide of fisheries are three of the problems facing the hub of the state's water system.

Recent studies show there is a high likelihood that a major earthquake could occur on a fault in or near the Delta. Such an event could lead to the collapse of the century-old earthen levees of the Delta, allowing sea water to intrude and rendering the Delta useless as a source of fresh water.

Water experts have called the Delta the state's worst source of drinking water. Declining populations of certain fish species also have prompted concerns about environmental woes in the Delta.

Water Interests

As the number of water problems has multiplied, so too has the roster of groups involved in the water debate. Naturally, urban and agricultural groups have long been part of the water picture. In fact, ACWA for decades has represented urban and agricultural water interests around the state. Appropriately, interest in water has expanded beyond traditional "water interests" to include environmental and other policy-oriented groups.

CONSENSUS AND CHANGING COMMITMENTS

In assessing the long list of water issues, it is important to recognize that not all of these issues are new. What has changed is the manner in which the various groups and institutions have chosen to deal, or not to deal, with the state's water problems.

Early in the state's development, agreement existed as to the necessity of planning for adequate, reliable water supplies. Water was a prominent component of public policy. Equally important, legislators exercised true leadership and vision in addressing the current and future needs—not only of their own regions but of the state as a whole. The public supported the funding for necessary water storage projects and facilities, and the administration had the political power to implement water planning and development.

In other words, the process worked; there was consensus concerning what needed to be done and the role each should play toward the ultimate outcome. The result was the authorization and development of the federal Central Valley Project (CVP) and later the SWP. Both projects employed the ethic of the need to store water during times of surplus in order to provide water in times of deficit.

The need to forge agreement from the midst of conflict and debate was evident again in November 1986, when the long-sought Coordinated Operation Agreement (COA) for the two projects was signed. The landmark agreement did not happen overnight, but it did eventually garner the endorsements of environmental groups, water contractors, agricultural water users and others.

Another illustration of a change in commitment as a result of public consensus is the prominence environmental protection has on the national agenda. This consensus has only begun to reveal its potential impact on all public policy issues.

The emergence of environmental priorities and a growing laundry list of complex issues impacting water agencies led ACWA to seek broad consensus among its own 400 members. After an 18-month effort, ACWA's members approved in November 1988 a comprehensive policy framework addressing regional concerns, in addition to the interests of both farms and cities. What resulted was a historic document, "Water for All Californians," which identifies the key water issues of the state and the corresponding policy approach to be taken by the association on those issues. ACWA uses this document as the first step in determining its position on legislation and other activities.

As a follow-up to ACWA's water policy, the association commissioned the Field Institute in March 1990 to conduct a public opinion poll to ascertain public consensus on a number of water issues, including water supply and distribution, quality, conservation, reclamation, environmental issues and growth. All successful consensus efforts must begin and end with public involvement. Up to that point, there was no baseline for the public's evaluation of water as a issue.

What we learned was that the public had strong and specific opinions about California's water and felt a personal commitment to conservation. There was clear consensus that water ranks among the top public issues. The information has been invaluable and has served as a catalyst for other specific consensus building efforts by the association.

In the recent past, it has been more difficult to point to many successful consensus efforts. Today, however, two promising examples do exist. For more than a year, representatives of urban, agricultural and environmental interests have been meeting in the Three-Way Water Agreement Process in an attempt to find common ground in resolving waster issues. More recently, Californians for Water has been organized. This group is also seeking to develop an acceptable consensus on resolving statewide water problems.

COMPETING AGENDAS SLOW CONSENSUS

At a time when environmental, economic and demographic pressures are clouding California's public policy picture, it has become more difficult in the 1990s for any one issue to rise above the clamor. With so many problems vying for available funding and attention by the state's leaders, water has struggled to remain a priority issue. Without due attention by the public, state leaders and policy-makers, consensus cannot develop.

When dealing with a limited resource such as water, the need to balance competing interests is especially acute. Consensus must begin within the framework of individual groups before the process can advance to the next level. This is where many efforts are stalled, as consensus at the grassroots level is not achieved. To be viable, the consensus process must involve all appropriate parties. Though there are benefits to involving many in the discussion of issues, divergent interests can also slow or even paralyze problem resolution.

Because water problems are often regional, and solutions often call for broader acceptance of policy, it is difficult to establish overarching consensus for resolving water problems. Agreement may exist in neighboring communities, but as you continue to move geographically, sensitivities to issues change and so too does the desired outcome. Proposed solutions tend to polarize more than the issues themselves. Problems in the Delta, are a prime example of a situation in which numerous regions and interests have much at stake yet have been unable or unwilling to compromise on the best solutions for all concerned.

CONSENSUS AND LEADERSHIP

The strengths of achieving sound water policy through consensus are obvious. It is an open process where the broadest array of perspectives are considered. Issues are addressed, solutions are identified and implemented. The process itself breeds compromise, support and ownership by those involved. It allows the construction of a framework within which more specific water issues can be addressed.

The process of consensus also has weaknesses. It is time-intensive, and often while consensus efforts are being played out, water problems can become more critical. Appropriate deadlines obviously must be established to prevent potentially devastating situations from worsening. Consensus efforts require that involved parties be willing to compromise and to give something up. This perhaps has become the root of our present gridlock.

Consensus is in no way a perfect process. But it has become increasingly clear, that perfect or not, we must strive to integrate consensus into problem resolution. We all must recognize the need to develop a policy framework based on public support. Balanced, forward-thinking discussions of the issues at hand have become not only invaluable elements of contemporary problem-solving, but also some of the most integrated, progressive paths to getting results.

But we should also recognize that leadership by our elected officials is an essential factor in providing incentive for various interest groups to reach consensus. No group will want to be left standing at the station while the effort to solve California's water policy gridlock is seen moving down the track.

USING CONSENSUS AT THE MACRO-LEVEL

Collecting and studying baseline data are primary orders of business in the problem-solving process. Here at the macro-level, consensus has the potential to help shape and synthesize the scope of future policy. Consensus building programs such as Californians for Water provide diverse groups with an opportunity to participate freely and rigorously in the long-term planning arena, where broad goals can be set and a road map to dealing with problems drafted.

The starting point on that road map? Agreeing on what can be agreed on. Parties interested in getting results should use this elusive yet attainable plateau as a jumping-off point, employing collective opinion to identify problems and formulate criteria to be used in considering solutions. This is not the time to argue over specific solutions—discussion of these should be handled separately. It is the time to use collective opinion to hammer out some sort of game plan for addressing whatever problems have been targeted.

LEAVE SPECIFICS FOR MICRO-LEVEL DISCUSSIONS

Having undertaken that, the focus of the problem-solving process can then turn to specifics. Once the groundwork has been laid for addressing problems and the criteria established of potential solutions, the discussion can shift to mechanics and hardware. Here, at the micro-level, consensus building is not an appropriate means to develop and implement specific action plans. In fact, because consensus is unlikely to emerge on the details of potential solutions, other decision-making techniques take on a new importance.

Public needs must be met and the environment protected; it is crucial that the public interest not be held hostage while interest groups continue to debate specifics at this point. If results are to be achieved the process at this stage must turn to majority-based decisions to carry out actions, based on the criteria and baseline data derived by consensus in the previous phase.

As applied to California's water picture, an illustration of this two-stage process can again be drawn in ongoing efforts to frame and resolve Delta issues and other statewide concerns. Through consensus building activities such as the Three-Way Agreement Process, a framework of agreement on addressing such matters as water quality problems,environmental protection and allocation issues can be developed. By identifying problems and determining what ought to be considered as part of any potential solution, the process is set in motion and a useful template is cast for effecting change.

In the second stage of the process, consensus plays a diminished role and appropriate policy-making groups, such as the State Water Resources Control Board, the governor and the Legislature, should begin to discuss specifics. Based on the criteria spawned in the first stage, policy-making groups should develop proposals for solutions and move toward selecting the most feasible. Public input in the form of hearings or ballot measures is appropriate and should be sought once candidate solutions have been identified.

KEEPING ONE EYE ON THE BIG PICTURE

Interest groups involved in the consensus process should avoid absolutes. Efforts to identify problems and solutions should not become hamstrung by preconceived notions or endless disputes over specific solutions and their potential components. The public interest is better served at this stage by sincere, big-picture discussion of concerns and how they should be approached than by cynical and limiting criticisms of specific options that may or may not be feasible.

Some cities and counties in California have undertaken efforts to adopt policy statements. Groups interested in resolving California's water woes would do well to do the same. Each should identify what it is willing to bring to the table. In the 1990s, the big picture must be considered at every turn. Integrated solutions represent the most progressive way to address problems today; discussions should reflect that and recognize there is no one cure-all to the state's water complexities.

INTEGRATED PLANS HOLD THE KEY

Any formal water policy must combine the broadest range of water resource strategies. While isolated and arguably short-signed solutions have been the focus of various legislators and opinion leaders in recent times, the ultimate answer for California will be an integrated plan.

An integrated plan must include multi-level elements such as water banking and storage, conjunctive use, water conservation and management, voluntary transfers, reclamation and other technologies to bring about appreciable results. Progressive projects, such as the Los Banos Grandes offstream storage facility, have the potential to provide the "buckets" needed to meet our state's water needs. When combined with much-needed improvements to the Sacramento-San Joaquin Delta system, conjunctive use agreements and transfers are clearly a vital opportunity to get results. New and evolving technologies such as desalination should also be studied and integrated where feasible.

Gov. Wilson must lead the effort. The best-laid plans are likely to go nowhere without clear leadership at the gubernatorial level, as Californians have learned in past years. Indeed, the types of decisions facing our leaders today are distinct from those faced by visionary leaders of decades past who were able to act on a reasonably clear mandate from the public to construct our state's superior university, transportation and water delivery systems. Sharply divided publics such as those found today do not lend themselves to similar "visionary" decision-making. What's needed in the 1990s are leaders who are willing to assume the role of risk taker, forging ahead through sometimes murky waters to facilitate consensus.

Given the rapport Wilson has demonstrated with divergent groups, he may emerge as a major force in bringing a spectrum of interests together. Wilson should move to position himself as the "consensus governor" with water as a top agenda item. By acting with dispatch on water issues, as he did during the drought crisis, he will have the opportunity to lead consensus efforts and eventually advance solutions to the state's short- and long-term water problems. A move of this magnitude would surely be welcomed by all parties interested in shaping California's water future.

The effects of the drought can be seen in the low water line at Lake Oroville in February 1991. Lake Oroville is the start of the State Water Project which provides water to Southern California. Photo credit: California Department of Water Resources.

COMPETING INTERESTS FOR CALIFORNIA'S WATER

Agricultural, Environmental and Urban

Agriculture

California boasts of some of the most productive agricultural land in the world. As the state works towards solutions to its growing water problems, many in agriculture feel that their water is an obvious target for growing urban areas. With agricultural water consumption at 80 percent of the state's developed water, it may seem that only slight conservation on farms will free-up large amounts for urban areas and the environment.

But the agriculture industry says it is doing all it can to use water efficiently. It is simply not economical for farmers to waste water. Many in the industry will concede that urban users and the environment need more water. But the answer to the water problems in California is more water development and facilities, not siphoning the agricultural water supplies.

In addition to water conservation and efficient use, agriculture is contending with two serious issues—ground water overdraft and agricultural drainage. Although several efforts are underway to contend with these problems, the solutions also have a water cost.

With the example of the state Drought Water Bank behind us, many are looking more and more seriously at water marketing. Although many fear "another Owens Valley," water marketing may provide some relief for the state and be of benefit to the farmers.

THE CALIFORNIA WATER DILEMMA: ACHIEVING A BALANCED PLAN

Jerald Butchert

The creation of a complex water supply and delivery system has been a boon to California. Our ability to transport water from north to south and east to west has transformed this mostly desert-like state into the most desirable location on the planet in which to live. Additionally, our state enjoys an economic strength that surpasses that of all but a handful of developed nations.

But while California has flourished, traditional water development has not. The very resource that helped make this a great state is now stretched to the limits of its ability to meet many competing water needs.

Unprecedented urban growth has pushed California's population to 30 million and this growth continues unabated. Sentiment grows to restore and rehabilitate vast areas of wetlands, as well as the river environments of the state. The Central Valley continues to suffer from a chronic problem of ground water depletion.

And yet, precious little is happening.

Jerald Butchert joined Westlands Water District, the largest water district in California, as general manager in 1977. He has also worked with the Fresno Irrigation District as chief engineer and assistant manager, as executive officer of the Eel River Water Council, and as the Metropolitan Water District's legislative representative in Washington, DC.

Decisions affecting California water policy have reached an impasse. The state's water delivery system is fast losing its ability to meet the present and future water needs of its people. The state has reached an era in which public concern for the protection and conservation of the environment is increasing. And California's agricultural industry, the largest water user in the state, is trying to maintain an adequate water supply amidst public resentment over perceived misuse of water.

California's governor has inherited this impasse. A primary challenge for his administration is to develop a strategy that addresses the state's water needs for people, for industry, for the environment and for agriculture in a manner that is fair, equitable and beneficial statewide.

AGRICULTURE'S PERSPECTIVE

Much of California's early water development encouraged the settlement of agricultural areas. By providing a reliable surface water supply, California spurred the creation of its largest industry—agriculture.

California has been the nation's leading agricultural state for 42 years. In 1989, the on-farm product value of the industry amounted to more than $17 billion, contributing more than $51 billion to our state's economy. In California, one in five people is employed in an agriculture-related business. In the Central Valley, that figure jumps to one in three.

The diversified industry produces more than 250 different crops and livestock commodities. Eleven U.S. crops, including almonds, dates, figs and olives, are grown exclusively in California. California's leading farm county, Fresno, ranks higher than 25 states in farm production. California's farmers provide more than 50 percent of the nation's fruits, nuts and vegetables on only 3 percent of U.S. farmland. Our farmers' innovation and use of modern technology help keep the citizens of the U.S. better fed for less money than anywhere else in the world.

While California's agricultural community is proud of its worldwide reputation for high quality and standards, none of it would be possible without a dependable water supply. Seasonal rainfall without long-term storage and conveyance facilities could not support California agriculture as it is today. Agricultural water use figures prominently in California's water policy picture. The industry requires large amounts of water to produce the food and fiber that all Californians and Americans eat and wear. Agriculture's use of water is often criticized. Some say farmers are inefficient and wasteful. Others say farmers should pay more for their water. Still others say irrigation produces salty and toxic drainage water. And some say low-value crops should be outlawed so that the water they use can be diverted for other purposes. While these problems need to be examined, they should not cloud the fact that irrigated agriculture is a highly beneficial use of the state's water.

Agriculture is an important industry for all of California. All Californians share in the benefits it provides. Agriculture is a resource worth protecting, and that means assuring a reliable water supply for farmers.

AGRICULTURE'S ROLE IN ACHIEVING CONSENSUS

Members of the agricultural community recognize their role in achieving water policy consensus in this state. While some in agriculture are guilty of being reactionary and/or unwilling to change, enlightened agricultural leaders also recognize that cooperation with and among all of California's beneficial water interests is essential. This cooperation is illustrated by the following examples.

Although it took several years, Imperial Irrigation District (IID) and the Metropolitan Water District of Southern California (MWD) finally announced a significant water transfer agreement, providing benefits for both agricultural and urban water users. Under the agreement, MWD will provide financing for IID to line its earthen canals, which are subject to seepage losses. In exchange, IID will transfer 100,000 acre-feet annually to MWD, the amount of estimated water savings from lining the canals.

Another example of urban-agricultural cooperation is the MWD/Arvin-Edison ground water banking plan. This conjunctive use plan, while not yet completed, has generated support from both the agricultural and urban water communities. In surplus water years, MWD will provide surface water to Arvin-Edison for irrigation purposes. In exchange, Arvin-Edison will forego pumped ground water and allow some surface water to percolate. In dry years, Arvin-Edison will provide its surface supply to MWD and rely on ground water for irrigation.

A third example of cooperation by an agricultural district is the recent transfer agreement between Placer County Water Agency and Westlands Water District. While these two agencies agreed to the transfer, the final outcome benefitted the American River fishery and the city and county of San Francisco, as well.

Westlands agreed to purchase up to 80,000 acre-feet of water, which otherwise would have been stored in Placer's Middle Fork American River Project. Among other things, the State Water Resources Control Board required Placer to release the water at optimal times for fish, coinciding with federal efforts to provide instream flows in the American and Sacramento rivers' systems for fish and other environmental enhancement.

Shortly after the agreement was announced, Westlands was contacted by the city of San Francisco, which needed additional water to meet urban needs. Westlands agreed to allow San Francisco to take any water available after the first 40,000 acre-feet was released for Westlands.

These examples demonstrate that agriculture is a willing player in achieving water policy consensus to help meet urban and environmental needs. Agricultural water leaders obviously want to maintain stable water supplies for their farmers; they also understand that creative transfers and exchanges that benefit urban and environmental needs are inevitable and, indeed, good for California's society.

California agriculture probably has reached its peak in terms of land used for crop production. In future years, agriculture will either maintain its current levels or, more likely, gradually decrease as urban populations continue to swell. As farmland goes out of production, water previously allocated for irrigation purposes may very well be used to fill swimming pools, wash clothes, improve river flows and meet other domestic and environmental needs.

In summary, agricultural water leaders are in a position to provide positive input to a process that results in win-win-win situations for farmers, urban users and environmental advocates. It is, however, essential that this attitude be shared by all competing water users.

THE CHALLENGE FOR THE GOVERNOR

Considering the state's numerous water dilemmas, California's governor faces an enormous challenge. There are two probable outcomes. The governor can wholeheartedly embrace this opportunity, take charge and direct the future of California's water policy decisions. Or, he can decline the challenge, steer clear of debate and allow this great state to deteriorate slowly.

The latter option is not desirable. The former, while not easily achieved, can be accomplished by adopting an approach that is sensitive and, at the same time, sensible.

When Gov. Wilson entered office in 1991, he faced a large amount of unresolved business. The state's budget was unbalanced. The Legislature was reeling from the potential implications of Proposition 140, as well as reapportionment. The governor had to create and develop a new staff. Transportation and education problems were growing. Finally, numerous social issues, such as poverty, homelessness and access to health care, had gained prominence and public sympathy. The governor had a full plate of issues to contend with right away.

Water managers recognized the governor's full agenda. They understood that, particularly at the beginning of his term, he had to focus his attention on setting his priorities and on developing relationships with the Legislature and his cabinet. The governor had to have a political support system in place before any strong action could be taken, regardless of the issue.

While the political aspects of the process are important, they also are well underway. On the other hand, the time span for addressing certain water issues is shrinking. There are two primary water issues that deserve immediate attention: conveyance improvements in the Sacramento-San Joaquin Delta, such as a Peripheral Canal, and additional surface and underground storage facilities.

California has experienced five years of severe drought. Even after the drought ends, water shortages will continue and probably last for longer durations. Our water delivery system simply has no additional capacity. It cannot move water efficiently, and it is constrained as to where the water can go. Improvements are desperately needed.

Water shortages will also continue because of inadequate storage facilities. There has been no major water development since the 1960s. Now, the lack of surface and underground storage facilities is catching up with us. California needs more water storage facilities soon.

The exact strategy for achieving water policy consensus is really unknown. It is also questionable whether true consensus can be achieved. Nonetheless, there are certain components that ought to be incorporated into a strategy that may contribute to results that are more "win-win-win" oriented.

A primary component is the governor's public recognition of California's primary water needs and a commitment to balance those needs. Typically, there are three categories of water needs: urban and industrial uses, irrigated agriculture, and environmental protection and enhancement. The governor has taken this step. Not only has he acknowledged the three competing uses, he has declared all of them to be beneficial uses of the state's water.

A second component already embraced by the governor is his willingness to confront and settle the differences between the regulatory agencies at state and federal levels. The fact that California has both a state water project and a federal one is not unique. Unfortunately, because it has both, it faces many fractious fights.

Congress' passage in 1986 of the Coordinated Operation Agreement (COA), for example, has not lived up to expectations. This legislation, which provides for the coordinated operation of the federal and state water projects, can become an important tool in the governor's implementation of a water plan. The governor should insist upon the completion of the terms of the COA.

A final component, and probably the most critical in terms of achieving success, is support from the governor. The governor has many issues to address; water is but one of them. Therefore, the governor must provide some direction for carrying out his water plan. Whatever course the state policy-makers embark upon, it may end up nowhere unless precise direction comes from the governor.

Gov. Wilson must support consensus-building efforts such as the ongoing process involving urban, agricultural and environmental water leaders. These efforts, combining input and feedback from leaders in the urban, agricultural and environmental communities, may flounder unless they are supported and embraced by the governor.

The ultimate plan for managing California's water resources must have the governor's support. His support is critical for balancing the various water needs, addressing federal/state regulatory issues, providing solid direction for action and supporting new public policy efforts. By bringing together the various water interests in a process for developing water strategies, the governor can lead the state toward water compromises that benefit the urban population, keep the agriculture industry strong and enhance and protect the environmental resources. None of these needs have to be mutually exclusive. The governor should be the one to bring these various interests together for directed, positive change that's beneficial for all.

An aerial view of Shasta Dam, the source of the Central Valley Project, during the 1950s. The reservoir is full, unlike the start of the 1990s, when the drought and releases to protect the spawning fish have brought down the level of the lake. Shasta is the source of the Central Valley Project, operated by the U.S. Bureau of Reclamation. Photo credit: Bureau of Reclamation.

WHY WATER MARKETS ARE GOOD FOR CALIFORNIA AGRICULTURE

Frederick Cannon and Ronald H. Schmidt

The farm community in California has viewed skeptically the calls by economists and others for the development of a regulated water market in the state. While voicing support for the concept of markets—after all, markets are used to allocate most goods and services, including food—farmers and farm organizations often voice concerns about the negative impacts of water sales on rural communities.

Despite these concerns, however, a properly developed water market will support a stronger farm economy and stronger rural communities in the future. Under a well-regulated market system, water rights would be secure, so farmers would not have to worry about voter initiatives, environmental challenges and federal and state legislation that threaten their access to water. In addition, shifting from the current allocation system to a market-based allocation system for water will allow funding for needed improvements in irrigation technology, support the development of projects to address drainage problems and create investment opportunities in higher-valued crops.

In total, the improvements in California's irrigated agriculture from the development of a regulated water market will far

Frederick Cannon is vice president and senior economist at Bank of America in San Francisco. Ronald H. Schmidt is senior economist with the Federal Reserve Bank of San Francisco.

outweigh the effects of any reductions in the amount of water used to grow crops in the state.

FARM CONCERNS AND THE OWENS VALLEY SYNDROME

One major reason that state water policy has not more readily adopted market strategies is the fear that water-thirsty cities will dry up California farms. Farmers' concerns about the impact of the change in use of water on local communities—farms being replaced by housing tracts—originate from their fear of what could be called the "Owens Valley syndrome." Early in the century, the Los Angeles Department of Water and Power obtained the rights to much of the Owens Valley water (the Owens Valley is a region on the eastern side of the Sierra Nevada) by buying Owens Valley farmland. To this day, many farmers feel that this was a lost battle in the California water wars, and a potentially rich agricultural area was reduced to economic obscurity.

Fears of "another Owens Valley" are reflected in the policies relating to water transfers of farm organizations. For example, the California Farm Bureau's policy on water marketing and transfers supports water sales providing that "the water needs of areas of origin of surface and ground water are first evaluated and appropriate protections of these entities are assured."

Although such policies reasonably address concerns about local economic impacts, they can impose large constraints on markets. Essentially, under current application, such policies would require proof that the community where the water is sold will be unaffected by the sale. Such a requirement is analogous to requiring that a Sutter County rice farmer show that all the residents of Yuba City have enough food before he or she can sell rice. In a regulated water market, the effects of water sales on local economies can be addressed without imposing such constraints.

Indeed, despite fears of community deterioration, farmers and farm communities have a lot to gain and little to lose from a water market. In fact, the Owens Valley controversy developed because there was not a regulated market for water use in the state, and cities were forced to buy up farmland to obtain water. In a clearly defined water market, cities would not buy up whole regions or farmland, but rather would buy incremental amounts of water from farmers, primarily during dry years. A water market would also create incentives that would allow farms to use water more effectively and give farmers the capital to address long-term resource needs. And it is important to remember that markets are voluntary—no one will force farmers to sell their water.

The worry that agriculture in California will be replaced by homes in southern California is exaggerated. According to the Department of Water Resources, farms use an average of 28.5 million acre-feet of water annually, and cities use an average of 5.5 million acre-feet. Thus, a shift of 2.75 million acre-feet, or less than 10 percent of the water now used in agriculture, from farms to cities would increase urban supplies by 50 percent.

Water from the Central Valley project is used to irrigate this cotton field near Tranquility in California's San Joaquin Valley. Photo credit: Bureau of Reclamation.

This relatively small shift in average water supplies suggests that water prices would not be significantly affected by moving to a water market. In wet years, the water price would be lower than current levels and little water would move. In a dry year, the price would rise and significant amounts of surface water would move from farms to cities, and farmers would rely on ground water. Estimates of the responsiveness of agricultural water use to water prices suggest that a 10 percent decrease in water use would require, at most, an increase of 20 percent in average prices.[1] That increase would not be sufficient to price farmers out of production.

Moreover, while some farmers would choose to sell water at these higher prices, in most years the price increase is not likely to be large enough to make it worthwhile for farmers to stop farming. Potential profits from selling water would encourage conservation and investment in water-saving technologies by farmers, but the price would not justify removing their land from production and foregoing their agricultural production.

THE MARKET CONCEPT

Many of the farm concerns about a water market are fears of the unknown. Much analysis of water policy discusses *why* a market would work, but there is little analysis of *how* a market would work. A market-based water allocation system would not be an unregulated system. The nature of the industry suggests that it would be best designed and operated like other utilities.

A properly developed market would automatically sort out the competing uses for water and deliver the water to those who put the highest value on it. As prices rise, the market sends signals to individuals to find ways to conserve water—in whatever way is easiest for the individual—and they send signals to others that new facilities may be profitable enterprises, thus augmenting supplies efficiently.

The water transportation system is a natural monopoly and as such would be regulated like other utilities. In addition, environmental baselines would have to be in effect for a market to operate. Nevertheless, holders of water rights should be able to freely sell their current and long-term rights in a market. Markets such as those used to trade oil, natural gas or bulk electrical power offer models of how such a market can be structured.

A market would provide incentives to farmers to change their crop mixes in drought years, to idle some land and to invest in more efficient irrigation equipment. Urban users would be encouraged to use water more carefully and to install more efficient water-using devices when they recognize that their water bills rise as supplies become tighter.

Markets facilitate trading by relying on decentralized decision-making. Prices signal the collective value placed on water to all potential water users. Individuals can then choose their own consumption in light of that price and make water use decisions individually and voluntarily. If demand exceeds supply, prices will rise until a balance is achieved. Sellers do not have to find buyers individually: the market provides a meeting place.

By relying on individual decision-making, a market will allow users to evaluate their needs for water and weight those needs against the needs of others. Those who can reduce consumption at minimal cost will do so when supplies are low. And they will be compensated by those who find it more difficult and costly to reduce consumption.

As a result, market solutions offer the least-cost mechanism to address water allocation. A market will make sure that water goes to the highest-valued uses and will encourage conservation, so water is not used ineffectively.

In the case of California water, this advantage could save billions of dollars for residents of the state. If water is allocated more effectively, development of costly new supplies can be avoided. Plans for expensive new dams, canals, desalination plants and underwater pipelines from Alaska can be shelved, unless the price that would prevail in the market can justify such expenses.

The advantages to agriculture of a market approach would be particularly large during drought periods. Until the development of the governor's water bank, the current administered approach attempted to adjust to drought periods by managing farm practices. For example, in 1991 state policy-makers proposed allocation rules that would have restricted irrigation of trees and permanent planting to allow them to survive, but not produce a crop. Others called for state policy to restrict the production of certain water-intensive crops, such as rice or hay. And the water projects simply cut deliveries to farmers across the board, regardless of need.

In these examples, the current regulatory structure was attempting to replicate what would happen more easily and at lower cost in a market environment. The market approach takes the opposite stand. It starts with the logical assumption that farmers know the most about growing crops and raising livestock. From that assumption, it is easy to jump to the best way to determine water use by agriculture—give the farmers the correct information. In this case, that means letting them know the value of water, which is best signaled by its price.

Under a water market, bureaucratic meddling would be unnecessary, and costs imposed on farmers in the present system could be avoided. A market automatically adjusts to increasing water scarcity: water prices rise. Farmers that can conserve water do so and are compensated by selling that water to those that need more.

In severe drought periods, farmers might fallow some land or only irrigate high-value crops. As non-agricultural demands for water rise over time, slowly rising prices of water will encourage further conservation and investment in new technologies. The key advantage of the market approach, therefore, is the fact that farmers will be encouraged to use water in the best interests of the state—using more when water is plentiful and less when it is not—and they are compensated for their actions.[2]

BENEFITS OF A WATER MARKET TO CALIFORNIA AGRICULTURE

The development of a regulated water market in California would provide substantial benefits to California farmers and farm communities. There are three primary reasons for the benefits.

First, the development of a market requires secure property rights in water for farmers. Second, the ability to voluntarily sell water for compensation will give farmers the incentive to use water more effectively and give farmers access to a new source of funds, enabling them to address drainage problems and to invest in irrigation technology. Third, markets can reduce the financial risk to agriculture—both in the short- and the long-term.

Secure Water Rights

The first step in moving to a market is the most important: establishing clear rights. Once the political process had decided the most equitable allocation of water, that allocation needs to be codified. That is, the owner of a water right needs to have clear title to that resource.

Currently, some farmers may own rights to use water, but they cannot sell it directly. Instead, others in the same water district may have junior rights and can take the appropriation if the senior rights holder does not use the water. Markets work best when the agent making the decision has clear title to the water and can choose whether to use that water or to sell it. Thus, a water market requires solidifying water rights.

Moreover, it is possible for the current system to "oversubscribe" existing supplies. For example, some water districts are not allowed to draw their full allotment of water from the State Water Project, while at the same time, environmental groups argue that not enough water is available to protect fish and water quality.

Therefore, shifting to market allocation for water requires two fundamental changes in state water law. First, all rights need to be assigned with certainty. There can be no question about the ownership and ability to sell water. Second, the system cannot be oversubscribed. Allocation of rights must match available supplies.

Redefining water rights and allowing resale would be a fundamental change in those rights. Once granted, the rights could not be "taken" or revoked by the state, although the state or other water users could buy back those rights. A market eliminates the need for an arbitrary "public trust doctrine" that has reduced the security of water rights for both urban and agriculture users. Because "higher and better uses" can be reflected in the willingness to pay for those uses, changes in water needs can be accommodated through the purchase of water rights by those consumers whose needs are growing and also directly compensate those who are giving up that water.

Water experts agree that any change in water rights would recognize the claims of existing rights' holders. In most cases, historically-based rights would give farmers the option to resell their water to cities. Thus, farm water rights must be secured for a market to operate. Furthermore, market sales would always be voluntary. Thus, with a market, farmers' fears of having water taken from them would be alleviated.

Some farm interests have expressed fears that farm profits from water sales would create public resentment. Indeed, if the facts were not otherwise, the potential windfall of granting rights to farmers could raise major fairness problems. But the facts are otherwise. The economic effects of making this distribution of rights will be relatively small. Price changes from allowing resale to the cities are likely to be minimal. Even in drought years, water prices are not likely to rise much.[3]

Consequently, a water market will not lead to farmers selling vast quantities of water to cities at high prices. Instead, farmers will have an incentive to save a comparatively small amount of water and be compensated for investing in those savings. In all likelihood, most of the new needs for water could be satisfied with changes in agricultural practices.

Reducing Risks

A market also offers the potential to reduce or eliminate two important risks to farmers. First, in the short-term, market institutions would emerge to allow farmers to pass uncertainty about water supplies to other parties. Second, by creating a viable, adjustable mechanism to assure proper use of water in the state, there is less of a threat of political efforts to take agricultural water without compensation.

Once water is traded in a market framework, there is nothing to prevent futures markets from developing. Such markets would allow farmers to hedge their bets—as those in other parts of the country do with their final products—by entering into futures contracts (even buying or selling options). A farmer who buys water can purchase that water at a guaranteed price before entering the planting season (or, at least, use the information about prices to help make those decisions). Or, in the case of a farmer who sells water, fears of a drought that drives up prices can encourage the farmer to idle some land and sell the water at that higher guaranteed price. Thus, they avoid the risk of deciding to fallow land and find that late rains suddenly make their water worth less than they expected.

Over the long-term, a market clearly is in the interest of farmers. The status quo is not sustainable. Population growth will continue, and urban and industrial needs for water will increase. The costliness of enforced conservation policies on urban users ultimately will raise the threat that political forces in the cities—where most votes are—will seek to take the water through the initiative or legislative process.

Reinvesting in Farms and Farm Communities

The largest benefit accruing to farm communities from a water market will be a stronger farm economy. Under the current water allocation system, farmers lack an incentive system to make the most effective use of water resources. In addition, the status quo does not work for farm communities because current agricultural drainage issues remain unaddressed.

Faced with the market value of the resource, however, farmers would have the proper incentives to economize on their use. That would mean adjusting their crop mix to match water availability. During dry years, they would be encouraged to use less water and plant less water-intensive crops. Some acreage might even be idled. But most importantly, farmers would be given the incentive to innovate. Farm publications already are reporting on the adoption of laser leveling, drip irrigation and "surge irrigation" techniques. As we have seen in countless other markets, when the incentives are there, new inventions and methods emerge.

Indeed, much of the irrigated farmland in the state faces reduced future yields without changes in water practices. Many farms need to make large capital improvements in order to avoid salination of soils and high water tables. The best potential source of that capital for farmers would be the sale of some portion of their water.[4]

CONCLUSION

Perhaps the most encouraging development of the drought was the success of the water bank set up by the governor's Emergency Drought Task Force. The governor chose to set up a water bank to buy and sell water during the drought to address immediate needs, rather than decide water allocation by bureaucratic initiative. The water bank purchased nearly 800,000 acre-feet of water for delivery. Although this is only an early indication of the potential for a water market, and refinements in the development of a market are necessary, this experiment illustrates how a flexible water market could be developed to address the state's increasing demands for water.

The development of a regulated water market would be good news for California agriculture. Some in the farm community fear that the result would be the replacement of farms in the Central Valley with homes in southern California. In fact, farmers have a lot to gain and little to lose from a water market. First, farmers need financial resources to address declining soil productivity that results from the lack of drainage and high salinity in the soil. A water market could provide such financing. Second, not very much water has to be sold. A shift of less than 10 percent of the water now used in agriculture would increase urban supplies by 50 percent. Third, a water market will give farmers an incentive to use water more effectively and to install high-tech irrigation systems that use less water and increase crop yields.

REFERENCES

[1]Vaux, H.J. and Richard E. Howitt, "Managing Water Security, an Evaluation of Interregional Transfers," *Water Resources Research* 20:7 (July 1984): 785-792.

[2]Schmidt, Ronald and Frederick Cannon, *Using Water Better: A Market Based Approach to California's Water Crisis*, Bay Area Economic Forum, September 1991.

[3]Vaux and Howitt.

[4]Dimar, Ariel and David Zilberman, *The Economics and Management of Water and Drainage in Agriculture*, Klumer Academic Publishers, 1991.

Sprinkler irrigation is used on orchards in the Sacramento Valley. Photo credit: Larry Cumpton.

CALIFORNIA FARM WATER COALITION: ACHIEVING CONSENSUS ON WATER POLICY

Stephen K. Hall

It has been said so many times, and yet it seems to slip from people's minds unless it is constantly reiterated. Farmers don't use water. The people who consume farm products use the water that irrigates farm crops.

Thus, when California agriculture approaches the matter of water policy, it does so not only on behalf of farmers, but for all the people who are dependent on agriculture's products, which is to say nearly every person in the state and many beyond its boundaries. The ability to capture, store and distribute water in California has created the most amazing "food machine" in the history of mankind. California is a cornucopia that provides food and fiber of such quality and in such quantity that it has set a standard to which the agricultural sectors of the world aspire.

And yet, the natural environment in which this food machine functions is not inherently hospitable to agriculture. Particularly in the southern end of the state, the climate is semi-arid with not nearly enough precipitation to sustain most crops. Ironically, it is this condition that contributes to the ideal conditions for growing many crops. In California's central and southern valleys, the Sacramento, the San Joaquin, the Imperial and the Coachella, it is

Stephen Hall has been executive director of the California Farm Water Coalitions since 1989. He has been a member of the State Reclamation Board since 1983. Before his career in water resources, he worked on his family's farm in Kern County.

the ability to precisely control the amounts of water used to irrigate crops that contributes to the bountiful yield of those regions. The state's climate, the composition of its soils and the ability to closely regulate water flow to crops all converge to make California a state-of-the-art agricultural state.

Ensuring the flow of water to agriculture has never been easy. Farmers were among the first to capture and divert water, but as early as 1905 cities were in hot pursuit of the water developed by farmers to supply growing urban populations. That was the year the city of Los Angeles filed for water rights on the Owens River and its voters passed a $1.5 million bond issue to pay for the necessary surveys. Two years later, the same voters approved $23 million for construction. Los Angeles began purchasing land and accompanying water rights in the Owens Valley. As a result, much of the farmland was taken out of production. Area ranchers and businessmen, fearing for the area's agricultural future, resisted in every way they could, but it was a futile attempt to stop the inevitable.

Today, the search for new water resources by urban population centers of the state goes on. This time, it isn't just the water in the Owens Valley, or the snowmelt in the Sierra Nevada or the fresh water flows through the Delta that are being sought—it is all of these, plus the developed water that flows through the man-made canals of the State Water Project and the Central Valley Project.

And while this hunt goes on, the environmental community conducts its own search for more water. Environmentalists clamor for increasing fresh water flows through the Delta to reduce temperature and salinity levels in hopes of reviving the salmon and striped bass populations of that estuary.

And once again, they turn to agriculture as the source. "If agriculture used just 10 percent less water, the resulting surplus would be enough to supply every urban area in the state," goes the refrain heard from Sacramento to Washington. "In California, cows get more water than people. That's ridiculous!" Solve the cities' water problems by taking water away from the farmers, they say.

While some suggest we simply take the water by force of legislation, others are more subtle. Pending legislation would create a "free market" for water in which individual water users would be free to sell their water to the highest bidder. How could anyone argue with something so American—free-enterprise?

The bald truth is that the legislation is an attempted water grab that harks back to the days of William Mulholland and the Owens Valley. While individual farmers might profit from selling their water, the fallowing of land throughout agricultural regions could devastate local economies, that causing horrendous unemployment and lost income for entire communities.

Many in agriculture understand that the state's demographics are changing. California's population continues to grow at record rates. Urban areas, particularly in the south, are powerful magnets attracting people from all over the world. Seventy percent of the growth is from births. The cities' thirst must be quenched.

But can the thirst only be quenched at the expense of agriculture? Must we dismantle the amazing food machine that is California agriculture? Are there no other, less destructive, more intelligent alternatives available to policy-makers?

An environmental activist was quoted as saying there is no shortage of water in California, only a lack of intelligent water management. Agriculture agrees. We do not accept the notion that California is running out of water. Except during times of prolonged drought, there is more than enough water to serve all reasonable needs into the foreseeable future.

What is lacking, however, are the policies and the physical facilities that allow water to be managed in such a way that everyone wins and nobody loses. What we lack is a basic mind-set that everyone—cities, farms and the environment—is entitled to equal protection and that such protection is achievable, if we have the resolve.

If we pursue the "*let's take it away from farmers*" approach espoused by some, the result will be years of bitter argument in state and federal courts. The result will be further polarization of the state's urban and rural, northern and southern regions. The lawyers will get rich. The politicians will posture. The media will exhort. And, in the end, the people will lose.

Achieving consensus is the obvious and urgent need. The three major forces in the water wars must come to the negotiating table in good faith, with a willingness to compromise and to understand and appreciate the other's views and needs.

It is encouraging that such a process has been initiated. In what has come to be known as the "Three-Way Process," agricultural, urban and environmental water interests have been conducting meetings in search of potential areas of compromise. The process has been painfully slow and the prospects for ultimate success are questionable. The coming together of traditional adversaries is a fragile arrangement that could easily and quickly come undone.

And yet, many are pinning their hopes on the Three-Way Process. Gov. Wilson and his administration have encouraged the conferees and provided enthusiastic moral support to the consensus efforts. Politicians and appointed officials would love to see the process work. The media has expressed its wishes that the negotiations succeed.

Agriculture, through the California Farm Water Coalition, has made an enormous investment of time and effort toward helping the Three-Way Process work. If it turns out that the process fails in its mission, it will certainly not be due to a lack of support by agriculture.

What does agriculture want out of this process and what is it willing to give in return?

The single most important goal of agricultural representatives in the Three-Way Process is to ensure the long-term viability of agriculture in California. Agriculture's important contributions to the state's economy, its ability to provide affordable, high-quality food and its absolute uniqueness among the world's agricultural regions demands that its future viability be protected and enhanced. Accordingly, while agricultural interests will cooperate in the development of policies that result in overall improvements to the state's water system, such policies must not threaten the long-term viability of California's agricultural sector and the local economies dependent upon it.

With this goal clearly understood, a number of objectives are apparent:

* To ensure that adequate facilities are developed to provide reliable water supplies sufficient to maintain agricultural production and to meet future needs for food and fiber.

* To add facilities to provide additional supplies of local and imported water at reasonable cost.

* To reduce ground water overdraft through additional storage, conjunctive use and transportation facilities such that ground water remains an affordable, reliable source of agricultural water.

* To maintain local control over existing contractual and other water rights.

* To develop additional practical, locally-based water management programs that improve efficiency and optimize use.

* To protect the quality of agriculture's land and water resources.

WATER NEEDS OF MAJOR AGRICULTURAL AREAS

Although each agricultural area has differing circumstances, there are common elements that characterize the needs of the major agricultural areas of the state. The needs of specific areas are delineated below, with accompanying points on what they want and what they are willing to give in return.

1. Critically water-short areas, such as the San Joaquin and Tulare Lake hydrological basins, have local surface water sources (south Sierra streams) and some ground water, but those sources have not been enough to provide an adequate, long-term supply to sustain agriculture. State and federal project water has been brought in but not in the quantities expected. As a result, there is continuing ground water overdraft and periodic fallowing of productive land.

Need: These basins need improved supply reliability from state, federal and local projects such as offstream or other storage, plus conveyance, conjunctive use and Delta facilities. Some areas may also want to buy water from other agricultural areas that want to sell water.

Give: Many of these areas are willing to become partners with urban areas and other agricultural areas for additional development of local supplies through improved conjunctive use and conservation, even if those other areas get the larger share of the developed water. Farmers within this region may also be willing to enact dry-year options, in which they would pump more ground water or fallow land in dry years in return for cheaper or more plentiful water in wet years.

2. Areas with senior water rights, such as the Imperial Valley, the Delta, exchange contractors in the San Joaquin Valley and portions of the Sacramento Valley, have relatively dependable surface water rights and their shortages are less serious. However, they are on common water supply systems with growing urban areas and are concerned that their existing water rights may be seriously diminished or lost. In some cases they are limited in the crops their farmers can grow and cannot afford to pay high prices for water or install costly new irrigation systems.

Need: Farmers in these areas need assurances that they will not lose their water rights or be forced to give up their water involuntarily. Third parties and downstream water users will also need assurance that their legitimate interests are protected. These areas may also want financial assistance to improve their water delivery and irrigation systems.

Give: Some farmers in these areas want to sell or lease their water. Leasing the water is more likely than outright sale. Cooperative conservation and conjunctive use programs could also be developed. Where water can be conserved, that water could be transferred long-term.

3. Agricultural water agencies that share local supplies with urban areas generally have good water rights (Modesto, Turlock and Fresno irrigation districts are examples), but are faced with losing part of their water as urban needs increase.

Need: These areas need assurances that they will not lose established water rights and that transfer transactions will be on a voluntary basis. There must be an understanding in which urban areas sharing a common water source can't assume the availability of agriculture's water as a convenient reserve from which to draw whenever urban supplies run short. Relationships between ag/urban partners that allow greater conjunctive use and other development projects will help ensure that doesn't happen.

Give. These areas will provide water for growing urban centers within their immediate service areas. They may also participate in conjunctive use projects with major urban areas elsewhere in the state.

In summary, agriculture needs to minimize overdraft and other water shortage problems by developing additional water banks, offstream storage and water conservation projects and Delta facilities at reasonable cost. It needs partners who can afford to help finance such projects.

Agriculture believes that consensus should and can be reached. Agriculture wants to be part of the solution and correct the perception that it is part of the problem.

Ultimately, everyone who consumes the food and fiber produced by California agriculture has a stake in developing a consensus over water in California. Likewise, they have a stake in seeing that agriculture's needs are accommodated in any consensus effort.

LOOKING FOR A SOLUTION TO THE DELTA DILEMMA

David L. Moore

CALIFORNIA'S WATER SUPPLY DILEMMA

California produces more than 50 percent of the nation's fruits, nuts and vegetables on only 3 percent of the nation's farmland. This agricultural production, and the $16 billion annual income it produces, is in jeopardy. Ever-increasing pressure is being placed on the state's agricultural water supplies as California's population grows and the belief grows among many that, since agriculture consumes the majority of the state's developed water, a portion of this water should be diverted to urban uses.

SURFACE WATER DEVELOPMENT

In the 1880s, California's first state engineer, William Ham Hall, developed the concept of California's present-day water conveyance system. The mammoth Central Valley Project (CVP) was first conceived as a state undertaking, but the state did not have the means to finance such a project and it was ultimately

David Moore is president and chief executive officer of the Western Growers Association, a regional agricultural trade organization. From 1956 to 1987, he operated a potato packing and shipping operation. He has served on numerous economic and agricultural advisory boards.

constructed by the federal government during the 1930s through the 1950s.

By the 1950s, it became apparent that additional water development would be required to supply the rapidly growing areas of southern California and the west side of the San Joaquin Valley. The State Water Project (SWP) was constructed by the state Department of Water Resources (DWR) in the 1960s to serve those areas. Today, it is essentially completed except for a trans-Delta facility and additional storage to provide 4 million acre-feet. The plan is for the SWP to ultimately deliver in excess of 4 million acre-feet of water to agricultural and urban water users from the south Delta to San Diego. Water management in the southern San Joaquin Valley involves a high degree of coordination among a large number of federal and state agencies.

WATER SUPPLY AND USE

Californians' developed water supply is about 33 million acre-feet per year and water use is about 35 million acre-feet with the 2 million acre-feet shortfall coming from overdrafting ground water supplies. Some critics of agriculture state that agriculture is a sponge and will wastefully use all the water that is made available to it. The fact is that there is little undeveloped land available for agricultural expansion and the current trend indicates a reduction as agriculture gives way to urbanization.

There are areas of the state, such as Santa Barbara and San Luis Obispo, that have been subject to severe water rationing. Invariably, however, when water shortages occur they are first experienced by agriculture which, when possible, reverts to increased ground water pumping. A further burden on agriculture is that by law, and in the case of DWR water service contracts, the first cut-backs on deliveries are imposed on agriculture.

This philosophy is never more apparent than with the water quality phase of the Bay-Delta Estuary Proceedings conducted by the State Water Resources Control Board. If the principles set forth in the State Board's draft plan are a reflection of its position concerning the balance of beneficial uses and the fair allocation of water, agriculture should be concerned that the ultimate plan for the Delta and the water rights decisions that might follow will result in agriculture losing further ground. There is no mention in the plan concerning the importance of providing adequate water supplies for agricultural or even urban uses, by a means such as a cross-Delta facility; it only discusses ways to reduce the export of water for the Delta.

It is forecasted that there will be 40 million people in California by the year 2010 who, under the prevailing philosophy in the state, will have to get by with a supply that presently serves 30 million. Instead of planning ecologically sound water development projects, water users are being asked to do without and conserve, which has its limits. Some people have suggested that, when conservation has been carried to its limit, urban users will look to agriculture to provide water.

If no new water is developed for the state, shortages and rationing will occur on a regular basis. DWR has estimated that there will be water shortages in the SWP in 50 percent of the years. When the SWP was conceived, the state entered into contracts with various entities in the state and committed, upon completion of the project, to supply 4.23 million acre-feet annually. Presently, even in normal years, it can supply only about 2.4 million acre-feet annually.

AGRICULTURAL WATER CONSERVATION AND EFFICIENCY

Many suggest that water conservation is the total solution to overcoming the state's water deficit which is presently in the form of ground water overdraft. Others believe conservation, already mandated by federal and state water purveyors and the laws of economics as water costs escalate, is only a partial solution. These divergent views occur partly because of special interests, but mainly because of misunderstandings over the uses, reuses and final destination of water. About two-thirds of the water applied to agricultural crops returns to the underground for eventual reuse. On the other hand, the majority of the water diverted for domestic uses in the coastal communities where the majority of the state's population resides, flows to the ocean from sewage treatment plants. High water prices and other costs associated with irrigation provide an incentive to use water wisely, but the major incentive to conserve water is its scarcity, a factor that will be more and more prominent as water shortages increase. Escalating energy costs also play a major role in water conservation. As the cost of pumping ground water and boosting surface water increases, there is natural incentive for more efficient use. It is a commonly accepted fact among water experts that agriculture is using its water resources as efficiently as is practical.

The following, taken from *Agricultural Water Conservation in California*, written by Professors David Davenport and Robert Hagan and published by the University of California, Davis in 1982, is a summary of the state of water conservation in California.

1. The often-heard claims of achieving a 10 to 50 percent savings in agricultural water use are unrealistic as a means of reducing the state's net water deficit because they usually fail to distinguish between recoverable and irrecoverable water losses and thus include water that is available for reuse.

2. Only by reducing the irrecoverable water losses can the state's net water deficit (presently represented by the 2.3 million acre-feet of ground water overdraft) be decreased in the absence of importing new water after supplies.

3. In the San Joaquin Valley's agriculture, these irrecoverable losses go mainly to: a) the air as ET [evapotranspiration] (mainly crop transpiration) and b) highly saline water tables. Some consider percolation into presently "moisture deficient" subsoils as irrecoverable because years will be required to saturate this material before percolating water could be recovered. Because the area of such soils now irrigated in the San Joaquin Valley is

limited and deep percolation observed on such soils is small, these losses are of lesser importance.

4. If crop production is to be maintained, reductions in ET losses are feasible only as reduced evaporation (E) (Efficiency) losses.

5. The realistic potential for reducing E and flows to highly saline water tables probably approximates 2 percent to 3 percent of the water applied in agriculture, but the technical and economic feasibility of achieving even this reduction needs to be explored, including an assessment of whether E savings will be later partially lost as transpiration.

6. Therefore, the state's net water deficit, mainly overdrafting of ground water, cannot be offset solely by agricultural water conservation if crop production is to be maintained at present economic levels.

THE SAN FRANCISCO BAY-SACRAMENTO-SAN JOAQUIN DELTA ESTUARY

The watershed of the Bay-Delta Estuary supplies two-thirds of all the water consumed in California, including 40 percent of the state's drinking water. Two major water distribution systems export water from the Delta. These systems are the SWP, which originates principally from Oroville Dam on the Feather River, and the largest component of the federal CVP, Shasta Dam on the Sacramento River. Together, these facilities supply about half of the storage capacity in the Central Valley. Many other projects and over 7,000 water rights holders who divert water upstream or directly from the Delta also alter the flows into and within the Bay-Delta Estuary.

The Bay-Delta Estuary problems are well-documented, the most significant of which are:

1. Decreased flows through portions of the Delta during dry years and/or months of high export in normal years which affect water quality and the fish spawning environment.

2. Deteriorating Delta levees, because of their organic origin, are decomposing and literally blowing away.

3. There is insufficient "freeboard" on many Delta levees to enable them to withstand wind and water erosion that comes with high flows.

4. Levee earthquake resistance is very low. The soils supporting the levees are especially vulnerable to liquefaction, a loss of soil strength during ground shaking. If liquefaction occurs, levees could fail, introducing high-salinity water into the islands. It is unlikely that there would be sufficient fresh water available to displace the high-salinity water.

5. Disinfections are essential to purifying drinking water. Delta water is high in organic matter. Organic matter reacts with disinfectants. Chlorine plus organic matter creates trihalomethanes, a carcinogen. The implication here is that there must be a significant improvement in Delta water quality if water that is to eventually be consumed by humans can continue to be exported from the Delta.

6. Over time, a small foreign clam (Potamocorbula) has been introduced into the Bay-Delta Estuary and is multiplying at a very rapid rate. The significance of the clam is that its food is the phytoplankton and zooplankton, the base of the food chain for the endangered striped bass and other species.

SUMMARY AND CONCLUSION

This author believes that the remedy to California's impending water supply crisis lies primarily in the Bay-Delta Estuary. This is truly a statewide problem and it is the duty of all the people in the state to remedy the situation. The simple fact is that there is sufficient water in the state to supply its needs for many years to come; it's just a matter of agreeing on a remedy and acting. Further, the first logical step in assuring California of an adequate water supply is to complete some form of a Delta facility which, if properly constructed, will improve and protect the environment of the Bay-Delta Estuary and assure exporters of an adequate supply of good quality water.

It is apparent that state water users must soon undertake the cooperative development of a solution to the Delta dilemma and endeavor to put the Delta in order. The condition of the levees that make up the Delta is approaching crisis proportions as nature's forces are fast returning it to a marsh.

KERN COUNTY VIEW OF A CALIFORNIA WATER CONSENSUS

Stuart T. Pyle

INTRODUCTION

The Kern County water community includes dozens, even hundreds, of people in Kern County who are active in the procurement and delivery of water for agricultural, urban and industrial purposes. These people are concerned about the continuing availability of the sources of water for Kern County because these are very basic to its economic viability. There are at least 25 water districts and entities that deliver water for agricultural use and many more that deliver to urban water districts and purveyors within the county. Some contract for water from the State Water Project (SWP), some for Central Valley Project (CVP) water, some hold Kern River water rights; all have an interest in maintaining both the quantity and quality of ground water. During the past two decades it has become evident that water issues are regional issues and Kern County, which is now home to 500,000 residents and irrigates nearly 1 million acres of farmland, stands as a regional unit to be represented in statewide water matters.

Stuart Pyle worked as a civil engineer and water resources planner with the Department of Water Resources for 19 years. From 1973 to 1990, he was general manager of Kern County Water Agency. He is now a consultant to the agency.

The Kern County Water Agency has participated in both the administrative and legislative efforts to find solutions to statewide water problems. One major current effort that the agency is involved in is participation with the 30 SWP contractors in the Bay-Delta water rights hearing process of the State Water Resources Control Board (SWRCB).

The crux of all the issues from a water supply point of view revolves around the controversy about whether to build works in the Sacramento-San Joaquin Delta to enable better management of the water resources with a reduction of damage and an increase in the survivability of important fish and aquatic resource. Kern County sees the economic survival of a large portion of its agricultural economy as directly tied to resolution of issues affecting the Delta.

The SWP was proposed in 1957 as the first facility to be constructed under the California Water Plan to deliver water to the growing urban population of southern California and to the productive agricultural lands in the San Joaquin Valley. Former Gov. Pat Brown has stated many times his intuitive political view that the SWP had to be a statewide project; that it had to provide statewide benefits; that it had to benefit the northern cities and watersheds and bring water to farms in the San Joaquin Valley; and that it had to serve the growing southern cities. A project serving only southern urban areas would never be approved by a statewide vote.

The Kern County Board of Supervisors, backed by many farmers and businessmen with visions of the future, rose to the challenge to participate in the SWP. Through a legislative act voted in by the citizens of the county, the Kern County Water Agency was formed in 1961 and entered into a contract for 1,153,400 acre-feet of SWP water. The agency has been active in all statewide water issues affecting the SWP since that time.

SWP water was first imported in 1968. In the years since operation began, over 17 million acre-feet have been brought into the area for agricultural, municipal and industrial uses. The project has been successful in reducing ground water overdraft, and the present estimate of the continuing long-term overdraft is about 300,000 acre-feet annually.

Primary objectives of the many Kern County districts in importing and managing water have been: to maximize the use of scarce water; to use irregularly occurring large amounts of runoff without building additional expensive storage reservoirs; to obtain the least costly source of water in any year; and to preserve ground water supplies for future use.

PROBLEMS FACING KERN COUNTY AGRICULTURE

Agriculture makes an important contribution to the economy of Kern County, as well as to the state. The sources of water supply available to Kern County are basic to the continuation of farming at its present level.

The continuation of agriculture at its present level is threatened by a number of factors that lessen the reliability of the presently developed imported supply, that prevent DWR from developing the facilities and project yield as originally intended, and that will increase the costs of water, making farming with imported SWP water uneconomical in some parts of Kern County.

A major problem facing Kern County agriculture is that the full supply of water originally expected when the SWP contract was signed with the state in 1963 is not available. The Burns-Porter Act authorized the basic elements of the SWP, including Oroville Reservoir, San Luis Reservoir and the California Aqueduct, which have been built and in operation since 1968. The project water supply was based on these reservoirs and the diversion of unregulated surplus water from the Delta, and 1 million acre-feet of water captured in reservoirs on the Eel River and diverted into the Sacramento River. The opportunity to obtain this water was lost in the 1970s when the Eel River was classified as a wild and scenic river.

The original project plan also authorized Delta transfer facilities to make it possible to convey water stored in Oroville Reservoir southward across the Delta with a minimum loss of "carriage" water and damage to the fishery. These facilities, originally planned as the Peripheral Canal and more recently as the through-Delta facilities, have not been completed. Without the Delta transfer facilities, the loss of striped bass by entrainment in the exported water became a serious issue. In the absence of a Delta facility, the SWRCB has required a reduction or cessation of pumping from the Delta during the months of April through July when the striped bass eggs and small fish are present. This shut-down period coincides with the spring snowmelt runoff to the Delta and results in loss of opportunity to operate the pumps to obtain the planned level of yield.

Another condition that reduces project water available for export is that the amount of water needed to maintain acceptable Delta water quality and a positive outflow from the Delta has proven to be greater than planned at the time the project was designed. These reverses in the original planning have limited the average yield of the SWP to about 2.3 million acre-feet as compared to the contracted yield of 4.2 million acre-feet.

THE WATER OUTLOOK IN 1960 AND 1990

Kern County agricultural interests and the Kern County Water Agency have been active participants in the statewide water development efforts during the past three decades. Some things have changed during that period. One significant factor is that agricultural development has peaked during that period— agricultural interests are no longer seeking additional water.

Agriculture in California has undergone many changes in the past 10 years. Until about 1980, there was continuous development of farmland. Through the years, the pattern was to develop new land along with new water to irrigate the farms. Then a series of economic factors, not just the lack of water, combined to make agricultural land development and farming a less attractive business decision. The amount of land farmed began to decline.

Public attitudes prior to 1960 were different than today. Since California undertook to provide adequate water supplies for all needs, it has become apparent that there are undesirable impacts on our rivers, lakes and wetlands, and there are competing public demands to dedicate water resources to environmental and recreational purposes, in addition to the strictly economic development valued prior to the 1960s. One result of this change in attitudes has been to rule out for future development a full 40 percent of the state's water supply. A basic fact of California water is that 70 percent of the state's natural fresh water occurs north of the latitude of the Delta. When 30 percent of the total occurring in north coast streams is dedicated to wild and scenic river status, the rest of the state is left to meet its needs from the flows of the Sacramento-San Joaquin River basin, as well as the tributary flows of the southern mountains. This, then, has imposed a new set of limits on water development that was not expected by the originators of the California Water Plan.

WHAT ARE THE SOLUTIONS?

On one side of this issue are the water planners and water suppliers, of whom Kern County Water Agency is one, who propose that basic to any solution is the construction and operation of water development facilities that would make it possible to meet both water supply and water resource protection objectives. On the other side are those who object to more development, strive for changes in how water is used, urge cessation of water use for some purposes and seek to have water that is now used for economic uses dedicated to remain in rivers, bays or wetlands to benefit natural resources. The latter propose that because the amount of water used statewide, about 35 million acre-feet, is so large, even modest savings through water conservation would release enough water to take care of other needs.

AGRICULTURAL WATER CONSERVATION

The story persists that the way to solve California water shortages is for the farmers to stop being wasteful and save more water. How many times have we read that agriculture uses 85 percent of the state's developed water supply and if the farmers would just cut back on the amounts they use by 10 percent, there would be enough water to meet the needs for continued growth?

This is an issue that has received a lot of serious attention by many technical experts. Every appraisal shows that the amounts of water that can really be saved are relatively small. Saving water by increasing farm water use efficiency may reduce overdraft on ground water basins, but under most conditions it does not create an identifiable supply that could be transferred to another area.

Farmers are, however, doing a lot to improve their use of water. The University of California Cooperative Extension Service, which sponsors county farm advisors, is continually working with farmers to upgrade their agricultural and irrigation practices. Many districts and farms are participating in the California Irrigation Management Information Systems (CIMIS) program headed by DWR. This program is typical of several that work with farmers to analyze and help improve their water delivery systems and practices.

Cost is the one factor that has a heavy influence on how farmers save water. The cost of agricultural water results from the cost to build dams to store spring snowmelt runoff, canals to transport it to farm areas and distribution canals to get it to the farms. Water costs in Kern County are high and contribute to the high irrigation efficiencies found there.

It is also generally true that water use efficiencies are lower in areas where farm water use is based on diversions from unregulated streams, or where reservoirs were constructed in the early years of this century. In these areas, water costs are low and lower-value forage and field crops may be grown. To change to more efficient irrigation practices changes the timing availability of return flows to downstream diverters or when the flows actually reach the Delta. This could reduce late-season flows that carry the return water.

TRANSFER WATER FROM AGRICULTURE TO CITIES

There have been many proposals to meet the growing water needs of urban areas by transferring water now used by agriculture to the cities. This is a companion to the water conservation proposals to meet water needs without building more water storage and development projects. Several means are espoused as ways to create transfers.

1. Develop sales and exchanges of water saved through water conservation. The Metropolitan Water District of Southern California (MWD)/Imperial Irrigation District program is an example.

2. Short-term transfers of developed water held by water right or project contract, not completely used for some period in its own service area.

3. Cooperative conjunctive use programs between urban and agricultural areas to better manage periodic excesses and shortages through ground water storage and extraction.

4. Purchase farmland or convert to an alternate type of land use so the water formerly used on the land can be sold.

5. Create a free market economy to allow water to be traded or sold as a commodity. This may require that ownership of water now held under water rights permits and licenses, or where water users receive amounts under contract from the water right holders, be transferred to individual water users.

6. Proposals, unspecified as to process, for governmental reallocation of water now used for "low value" agriculture production to "high value" urban use. Increase the cost of water, making some crops to be uneconomical and forcing some farmers out of business.

Most agricultural interests, including those in Kern County, would actively support the first three types of transfers mentioned. There is, however, general opposition to transfers by governmental reallocation or some type of repricing. Changes in the water right and ownership provisions of California water law would have destructive impacts on the financial structure of hundreds of water districts.

Water interests in Kern County have always supported water transfers, usually in the form of sales of water or water rights, or exchanges of water which require a payback in water rather than money. Extensive systems of canals, water originating from various sources and opportunities to store water and retrieve it from either surface or ground water reservoirs have been developed over the years. These make possible the water transfers that increase the efficiency of the water system.

ENVIRONMENTAL RESOURCES

It is evident that one reason for the current impasse is the negative impact of water development on fish and aquatic resources. There have always been attempts to mitigate for these impacts by providing fish ladders, flow releases, fish screens and fish hatcheries. Some of the efforts have been too little, some have been poorly executed. However, within the past decade, there has been a widespread realization by water planners that the expenditures and the efforts to mitigate for fish losses need to be increased.

There should also be a greater state interest in maintaining the Delta for environmental, economic and water supply purposes than has been accepted by state leaders. Over the years, the Legislature has been ready to pass policy statements propounding the state's interests in the Delta, but it has not followed through with the financial backing to meet these needs. For instance, the Legislature was fast to adopt legislation in 1988 to provide a source of funding from the SWP to restore and maintain essential levees in the Delta. This allowed it to sidestep an earlier general fund appropriation for Delta levees. But, on the other hand, the Legislature has never acknowledged or sanctioned a general fund obligation to provide funds for a Suisun Marsh restoration plan where a significant portion of the works goes beyond the basic responsibilities of the state and federal water projects. It should also be noted that the Legislature has not provided adequate financial support for the Department of Fish and Game to carry out scientific studies and other operations in the Delta to supplement SWP funds provided by DWR.

This situation is indicative of the reasons for continual conflict between environmental or fish and game interests and the water development interests. The environmental groups, working through the public input process over the past 20 years or so, have rightly sought a minimization of adverse environmental impacts, as well as correction of mistakes and restoration of damages caused by water projects. Somehow, the Legislature should accept the responsibility to financially support the maintainance of the aquatic resources of the state in the efforts to solve the state's water problems.

A CONSENSUS OF WATER ISSUES

The word "consensus" has crept into the vocabulary of water policy-makers in recent years. To most people, it means a general agreement that is accepted by the majority of a group and which the entire group will support or not oppose even though some do not accept the decision as fully representing their needs or desires.

Attempts to solve the impasse of the 1970s were made by all-inclusive agreements such as SB 200 in 1980, which was defeated in a 1982 referendum vote. The defeat of Gov. Deukmejian's 1984 water package bill, carried by Sen. Ruben Ayala and Assemblyman Jim Costa, soured that administration on water legislation for its entire term. In reaction to that experience, over the next six or seven years, DWR worked on a step-by-step basis by attempting to solve the problems one issue at a time. Suisun Marsh was an example of a resolution of issues because most significant objections were satisfied or withdrawn. The step-by-step program in the Delta has led DWR to prepare three separate plans for the north Delta, west Delta and south Delta. In addition, planning for Los Banos Grandes Reservoir project has been carried separately.

KERN COUNTY PARTICIPATION IN A CONSENSUS PLAN

As a result of the impasse in water development, that may be characterized as a conflict between efforts to develop water resources as opposed to the desire to restore and protect the environment, the issues to be solved have become more clear. First and foremost of these issues to solve is the Delta water transfer, water quality and fishery problems so that statewide water demands can be met and Delta environmental problems can be resolved.

Following is a list of issues that must be considered in consensus discussions and some evaluation of these issues from Kern County's point of view.

Reliability of Water Supply

The increasing liability of shortages in water supply because of DWR's failure to complete the SWP is the most serious issue facing Kern County water interests. As the water needs of MWD and other urban contractors increase in the next decade, agricultural water users will face shortages in delivery of their entitlement in three out of four years. Some of Kern Water Agency's responses to the pressure of shortages in SWP supply are:

1. Kern will actively support DWR in efforts to add cost-effective yield-producing projects to the SWP. Projects with the lowest cost-yield should be constructed first.

2. Most Kern water interests support DWR construction of Delta improvements, specifically Delta water transfer facilities, along with acceptable operating conditions as the key to solving Delta water supply and aquatic resource problems.

3. Increase in the cost of water to growers in Kern County will lead to continued high water use efficiencies, changes in crop patterns and the likelihood of some water districts reducing their entitlement to SWP water.

4. Kern will continue to make the best use of water supplies by conjunctive use of surface and ground waters. It will attempt

to receive maximum amounts of water exported from the Delta in the months when it is available without impacting in-Delta needs.

5. The agency will continue to participate in the SWRCB Bay-Delta Proceedings with the objective of preserving DWR's rights to maximize the yield of the SWP within provisions set by the SWRCB to maintain water quality standards in the Delta. The agency will expect to have access to excess inflows to the Delta to support its conjunctive use programs.

Water Conservation

1. Urban water conservation will be supported in Kern County through public school and media advertising programs.

2. Agricultural water conservation will be supported through programs, such as CIMIS and AGWATER, that will make practical information available to water users so they can improve their practices. The agency will continue to collect water use and agricultural data and to periodically evaluate water use efficiencies so that water users can be aware of accomplishments or areas of potential improvement.

Water Transfers

1. Water transfers are endorsed as a practical method of increasing the efficiency of the statewide water development system. The established water rights system of California should be maintained. Water sales and water transfers should not negatively impact third parties. Where compatible with water rights, any party with ownership of excess water should have the right to make short-term or permanent sales and should be assisted in these efforts by those who control water distribution facilities.

2. The agency, as guided by its policies and within the limits of its formation act, contracts and the guidance of public comments, will assist all water districts in water transfers, primarily within the county, and elsewhere to the extent such transfers are necessary for economic survival.

3. Kern County is a water-short area with a continuing long-term ground water overdraft. The agency's main interest in water transfers is to obtain supplemental water and to improve its use of water through exchanges.

4. The agency will cooperate with urban areas on water management programs, including water banking and water conservation programs where water may be saved that would otherwise be lost to non-usable ground water or drainage sumps.

Environmental Protection

1. The agency is not only dedicated to operating its water supply programs to comply with regulatory provisions in place to protect the environment, but also desires that its programs reflect prevailing public opinion to protect and maintain all valuable natural resources.

2. The agency supports SWRCB and DWR in setting water quality standards in the Sacramento-San Joaquin Delta to protect water quality for all beneficial uses, including fish and wildlife.

3. The agency will encourage and assist DWR in its efforts to establish programs in the Delta and elsewhere to mitigate the damages caused by operation of the project.

4. Survival of fish and other aquatic resources of the Delta at acceptable levels is seriously in question. The precise reasons for the decline of the fishery is unknown. The scope of the problems transcends the operation of the SWP and the CVP. The solution to the problems needs the support of all water users whose water supplies impact the Delta. It further needs the financial support of the state to represent the interests of all the people, in addition to the direct involvement of the water projects.

San Francisco Bay

While all natural resources of the state should be protected from the negative impacts of water projects, it does not appear that fresh water flow needs into the San Francisco Bay are well-defined or scientifically supported. The consensus process cannot proceed when San Francisco Bay interests refuse to recognize that all of California must look to the Delta as the only available source of water supply. It is not reasonable for Bay interests to demand that diversions from the Delta be reduced and fresh water outflows be increased without a scientific and economic basis to lead to practical decisions.

Agriculture as a Water Supply Source

1. It appears that in future years some agricultural land will go out of production in Kern County because of the increasing costs of water supply and pumping. As a result, some agency SWP water supply will have to be reallocated within Kern County. It is anticipated that transfers of agency SWP entitlement out of the county mainly will be temporary leases.

2. Agricultural water should not be viewed as the primary source of future water supplies as an alternative to other sources, including recycling, desalination and development of naturally-occurring water.

3. Drainage problems should not go unsolved to the point that farming on drainage-impacted lands would not be productive and the water supply could then become available for transfer to meet urban demands.

Reclamation

Reclamation of brackish water sources should receive consideration by all water supply agencies. Attention is being given to reclaiming treated sewage effluent by the reverse osmosis process in urban areas. Reclaimed brackish agricultural drainage water could also be a potential source of water for urban uses. When the costs of all the options for obtaining water are arrayed, it becomes evident that reclamation is near, if not within, the range of feasibility.

Construction of Facilities

The crux of the water supply issues comes down to two factors: on one hand, the dedication of all parties to support and establish programs and operations that will preserve and protect environmental resources and, on the other hand, the construction of facilities to make the necessary water available to meet the social and economic needs of the people of the state. If consensus is not directed at agreement on the construction of facilities and their operation to fulfill the water supply purposes, then a consensus plan has little chance of success. The alternative to the consensus process would be to accomplish authorization for construction of facilities through a political process. It is more likely that success would be achieved for water development through an initiative process supported by the southern California population than through a legislative process.

THE CONSENSUS PROCESS

Can California's serious water situation be solved by consensus? How should the numerous water development and supply interests come together with local and nationally supported environmental groups to draw-up a consensus plan that will meet both future water supply needs and restore and preserve the aquatic natural resources of the state?

In this writer's opinion, that will not happen on a voluntary basis. During the past two decades, there has been continuous, effective blocking of all water resources proposals, and demands for taking water away from developed projects and to rededicate it to aquatic resources are becoming more strident. If the north coastal water sources can be locked up, if water developed for urban and agricultural purposes on the American River can be required to flow down that river for recreational purposes, and if water formerly granted by water right permit to Los Angeles can be directed by court action to remain in Mono Lake, there appears to be no reason why environmental organizations would give up on demands for no more pumping from the Delta or appeals for all unregulated fresh water to flow into San Francisco Bay. Environmental groups are less successful in dealing administratively with scientific evaluation and problem-solving techniques. Their strength is wielded through the media and through popular, environmentally-oriented legislators.

On the other hand, DWR and the Department of Fish and Game, backed by SWP contractors and other water development interests, have acted responsibly throughout this period to propose and support both projects and operational programs that will serve the minimum water supply needs of all areas and, at the same time, provide significant improvements to the aquatic resources. Attempts to arrive at a voluntary, spontaneous consensus among all of the parties would stretch out endlessly unless controlled by some form of deadline.

If a consensus is to work, it must be with strong statewide leadership AND authority. Consensus among the water development and environmental groups will never be achieved without the further consensus of the governor's office and the Legislature. The closest that the state has come to this type of consensus was in the negotiations that led up to SB 200 in 1980. This was a negotiated consensus among the special interests, with the developers and environmentalists on one side and the power structure of the governor and Legislature on the other side. It fell apart because dissatisfied interests in two special interest camps joined hands to sink the legislation through a referendum.

Little change in this situation can be expected unless some type of strong leadership is exhibited. Such leadership could come from either the governor or the Legislature.

If the governor becomes forceful in this situation, he could rely on his appointees in the Resources Agency to manage the process. A workable arrangement might be a governor's commission on the pattern of the commission to review California water rights appointed by Gov. Edmund G. Brown Jr. in 1977. This would allow a balanced panel of policy-makers and negotiators from a wide variety of interests to manage the activity with staff support garnered from various affected state agencies. The governor could, if he desired, negotiate the resulting consensus proposal with the Legislature to the extent that legislative authorities might be needed to execute the proposals.

It is also possible that the Legislature would choose to dominate the consensus process by passing legislation to set-up a planning body of some type to formulate a consensus plan. If no leadership emerges that can develop adequate solutions, the only prospect is for the water development communities to muddle along for years into the future, losing ground on environmental issues, with the threat of water shortages and unusable water quality facing them. In that case, there are many indications that southern California water interests would resort to the initiative process to provide legal direction to DWR under its existing legislative authorization to take the necessary actions to provide an adequate water supply consistent with reasonable environmental protections.

The confluence of the American and Sacramento Rivers at Discovery Park in Sacramento is a valued recreational area. The Sacramento River is California's greatest inland waterway, providing 35 percent of the state's water supply and the spawning area for chinook salmon and steelhead trout. Photo credit: Water Education Foundation.

Environment

Because of a rich variety of ecosystems—from deserts to forests to coastal estuaries—California has a remarkably large and diverse natural environment. According to the Nature Conservancy, California has 5,200 native plant species, one-third of which grow only in California. The state is home to 748 vertebrate species, excluding salt water fish. Of these, 38 percent of the fresh water fish, 29 percent of the amphibians and 9 percent of the mammals are found nowhere else in the world.

It is this rich diversity of plant and animal wildlife that contributes to the quality of life in California. But the state's population growth and economy have often overpowered concern for its natural resources.

With the passage of the Endangered Species Act by Congress in 1973, the strength of the environmental interests in California has been growing until now they are recognized as full-fledged players in the continuing water debates. Many environmentalists believe that the environment has been compromised almost to death. Representatives for environmental interests are now determined to accept only guarantees and protection that will hold far into the future. This means an adequate, long-term supply of water dedicated to fish and wildlife and the preservation of natural resources. In addition, environmentalists are looking for correction and mitigation of past damages to the environment caused by water projects and developments.

As discussed in the following articles, there have been consensus building efforts that will benefit the environment. In the opinion of many, however, there is no longer room for concession and compromise from an environmental standpoint.

AN ENVIRONMENTAL OUTLINE TO SOLUTION OF CALIFORNIA WATER PROBLEMS

Gerald H. Meral

The history of water development and management in California has rarely been one of consensus or statewide agreement. Rather, it has been marked by litigation, bitterly contested state and federal legislation and hard-fought elections often decided by narrow margins. While there is little reason to expect this pattern to change, it would be desirable to have greater agreement among the various parties who are responsible for the water development of the state.

HISTORY

Major water development in California was born in controversy, turmoil and debate. The most bitterly disputed early water developments were the drowning of part of Yosemite National Park by the city of San Francisco for a reservoir and the desiccation of the Owens Valley and Mono Lake by the city of Los Angeles. Both these developments set the pattern of

Dr. Gerald H. Meral has served as executive director of the Planning and Conservation League and PCL Foundation since 1983. He was deputy director of the California Department of Water Resources and directed the department's energy and water planning efforts from 1975 to 1983. He has also worked with the Sierra Club, Environmental Defense Fund, Friends of the River and the Tuolumne River Preservation Trust.

exploitation of politically weak, remote and environmentally sensitive parts of the state by large and well-funded cities or agricultural interests. In the case of Hetch Hetchy Valley in Yosemite National Park, the city of San Francisco overcame John Muir and his small but influential Sierra Club to virtually annex and destroy part of America's premiere national park resource. At the Owens Valley and Mono Lake, Los Angeles, through force, manipulation and outright purchase, acquired water rights and dried-up agricultural lands, riparian and other habitat and greatly reduced the biological viability of California's largest lake.

The development of the federal Central Valley Project (CVP) and the State Water Project (SWP) followed very similar histories of confrontation. The state originally wished to develop the water supplies of the Central Valley, but an attempt to include public power development as part of the project led to a referendum sponsored by the Pacific Gas and Electric Company. Since most of the water from the Sacramento River was destined to serve Central Valley agriculture and Bay Area water users, the vote on the referendum was divided between supportive northern and hostile southern California. The CVP was approved only because the distribution of votes in 1933 was heavily weighted in the north. Even then, the CVP was approved only by a very narrow margin of just a few percent.

The development of the CVP by the federal government came at a time of high unemployment and a depressed economy. The Great Depression made quick development of major facilities politically feasible. But bitter disputes about the land, water and wealth distribution aspects of the federal project led to lengthy litigation and congressional re-examination. The continued lack of benefits from the CVP to small farmers on the west side of the San Joaquin Valley (there are virtually no small farmer beneficiaries) led to a hard-fought House of Representative floor vote as recently as 1990.

The CVP continues to be the villain to conservationists interested in preserving the fish and wildlife resources of the Central Valley. Nothing like the consensus movement has emerged regarding the future management of the CVP with respect to restoring the fisheries destroyed by the project.

The State Water Project was born because of concern about the federal policy favoring the provision of water to small farmers, the slowing pace of federal water development, the perceived need to export water to southern California (beyond the reach of federal facilities) and the desire of the state to control its own water destiny.

Governor Pat Brown's leadership made it possible to pass the authorization for the SWP through the fractious state Legislature. Although the Delta and northern California interests opposed the project, they managed to insert key provisions in the authorizing legislation. These included a grant program for small agencies (Davis-Grunsky grant and loan program) and construction of the project in a way which would maximize the rate of winter export of water from the Delta. This was to protect the Delta agricultural users, who irrigate mainly in the spring and summer, but it also had the effect of providing some protection to Delta migratory fisheries, as compared to what would have happened if a small aqueduct had been built. Nevertheless, it is generally agreed that SWP construction had a devastating effect on the Delta fisheries.

Even though these features were included in the project, the northern California voters rejected the bonds needed to finance it. Only the increased number of southern Californians allowed the bonds to pass by a margin of just a few percent in 1960. The bonds were rejected in almost every county north of Fresno where voters saw the SWP as an effort by southern California to export northern water.

Thirty years have passed since the people have voted for additional water development. In 1980, the Legislature approved a plan to construct the Peripheral Canal and related water facilities. The plan was rejected at a referendum by a huge margin due entirely to massive opposition by northern Californians. The opposition was lead by farmers opposed to the environmental protection provisions of the measure and by conservationists opposed to additional Delta water export.

In 1982, conservationists placed an initiative on the ballot to reform the way water is managed in California. It included ground water management, instream flow protections, water conservation and other progressive ideas. Plagued by a lack of funding, the measure was easily defeated by an irate coalition of agricultural and industrial water users.

Governor Deukmejian tried to abandon the Peripheral Canal and replace it with a through-Delta facility to be approved by the Legislature. Conservationists objected to the lack of environmental protections in the package and to the fact that the proposed facility appeared to be extremely damaging to the Delta environment. In the face of northern animosity and defections by farsighted southern California legislators, the Deukmejian package died in the Legislature in 1984. An attempt to revive it died a similar death due to lack of support by the governor and the water industry and the strong opposition of northern Californians and environmentalists.

Looking back over this long and fractious history, some important lessons can be learned. First, the presence of drought makes it easier for the Legislature to pass water bills. The 1928-1934 record drought undoubtedly eased passage of the Central Valley Project Act. The relatively intense 1959-1961 drought probably made possible passage of the State Water Project by the Legislature and the voters. And the 1976-1977 record two-year drought made the Legislature more eager to pass the Peripheral Canal bill. The state always has a lot of problems, and dealing with water only rises to the top of the agenda when the lack of water is apparent.

Second, only strong gubernatorial intervention results in the passage of water bills. The two modern examples are the governors Brown. Pat Brown personally made water part of his agenda and Jerry Brown allowed his water director, Ron Robie, to exercise near-gubernatorial authority to craft a water bill. The only reason the 1984 water plan had a chance was because Governor Duekmejian invested a large part of his credibility in it.

Finally, new water development has never and will never go forward as a matter of uniform statewide consensus. The only question is: Can the forces favoring the particular water policy change overcome those who oppose it? History shows us that any hope of complete consensus on this controversial subject is not only vain, but misleading to those trying to decide whether or not to get involved in the water issue.

THE PLAYERS

Sacramento Valley Irrigators. Sitting on the best water rights in the state and controlling several million acre-feet of high-quality water, the irrigators of the Sacramento Valley generally believe themselves above the water fray. They take what they need from the Sacramento, Yuba and Feather rivers and let those downstream have the rest. They are generally opposed to selling their water rights (at least publicly) and are especially inflamed when it is suggested that they allow more water to flow downstream to increase the amount of water flowing to San Francisco Bay in order to protect fisheries.

So far, they have also refused to manage (or even utilize) their incredibly valuable ground water resources, either for themselves or for environmental or export purposes.

Delta Irrigators. In some ways the most politically savvy of all farmers, through litigation and political influence the Delta irrigators for years have avoided paying for any of the water they use. They also have arranged for state and federal subsidies to repair levees which often fail during floods. But most central and western Delta islands are now far below sea level, up to 25 feet or more. The central and western Delta is certain to become an inland sea when a large flood or earthquake strikes. Some of the islands have been purchased by those seeking to fill them and sell the stored water to the SWP. Others are slated to become wildlife refuges to avoid further island subsidence. Still, in any final outcome, the Delta farmers are certain to make their influence felt.

San Joaquin Valley Irrigators. Most of California's agricultural wealth is derived from irrigation in the San Joaquin Valley. A mix of private, local, state and federal irrigation projects make these counties among the most productive in the nation. But the rapid expansion of agriculture in the valley has ended and most irrigators would be happy to keep what water they have, much of which is exported from the Delta. The two serious remaining problems are ground water overdraft and salination, and poisoning of west side soils and ground water due to lack of effective drainage. The San Joaquin Valley fails to speak with one voice due to its multiplicity of water supplies, thus reducing its political influence.

Imperial Valley Irrigators. Paranoia is the understandable attitude of these southern California desert farmers. It took six years of negotiations for them to accept tens of millions of dollars from the Metropolitan Water District of Southern California (MWD) just to improve the efficiency of their water system. Many are convinced that the time will come when a continued inability of southern California cities to import more northern California water will lead to purchase of Imperial Valley farmlands and the export of the 3 million acre-feet of water used in the valley to coastal southern California.

East of the Sierra. The city of Los Angeles appears to be nearly ready to accept the idea that half or more of the water exported from the Mono Lake basin must be allowed to flow into the lake to keep it from dying. Similarly, a large amount of the water exported from the Owens Valley now seems destined to maintain the vegetation on the valley floor. When these concessions are made, a water war almost 100 years old will slowly draw to an end, leaving Los Angeles more reliant on other imported and reclaimed water supplies.

Bay Area Cities. The San Francisco Bay Area continues to grow, making water managers there yearn for more pure Sierra water. The West Bay and part of the South Bay (reliant on Hetch-Hetchy) may make an attempt to export more from the Tuolumne River. This attempt will be met by furious environmental opposition. Litigation will almost certainly be the result, as well as attempts at legislation. The East Bay has won the right to divert at least some water directly from the American River, but local conservationists oppose plans to store it in a local reservoir. A more logical alternative would be better management of the Mokelumne River supply, coupled with purchase of Mokelumne water rights in San Joaquin County.

Southern California Cities. Led by giant MWD representing most of the coastal plain, southern California is now seeking additional supplies and is concerned about the quality of imported Delta water. The continued phenomenal growth of southern California, coupled with losses of water supplies from the Owens Valley and the Colorado River, have convinced MWD that something must be done to obtain additional water. MWD staff and directors are trying to determine which allies (other cities, environmentalists, irrigators) would be most successful in helping achieve a higher quality, more plentiful water supply.

Fish Supporters. Those who are dedicated to the preservation of the sport and commercial fisheries are not simply environmentalists. They are actually harvesters of the fish and thus have a more urgent and personal need to see them survive than the traditional conservation groups. The fish groups personally feel the tremendous decline in the striped bass, salmon and other species and are often more willing to try to "cut a deal" in their desperate hope to restore the fish population to its former high levels.

Environmentalists. Eight percent of the electorate considers itself "environmentalist" these days, and the organized groups have wielded that public opinion effectively, maintaining a high level of credibility with the public. The environmentalist agenda includes protection of wild rivers, restoration and enhancement of wetlands, fisheries protection (both commercial, sport and native species) and the general health of the Bay-Delta ecosystem. While these groups speak most powerfully to the Bay Area, which tends to believe the worst of water exports, southern California voters also are inclined to support environmental protection. With this support, environmental groups can act effectively to block harmful new water development projects in all parts of the state.

Like the fishing groups, environmentalists are irate at the tremendous decline in the Bay-Delta fisheries and will not stand for any new water development unless fish and environmental restoration is guaranteed.

The Public. The public wants to protect the environment, at least as long as water shortages don't get too bad. Thus, many in the water industry secretly (or not so secretly) pray for a drought to get the public in the right frame of mind for more water development. The public does not oppose environmentally benign water development: they want a secure water supply, but only if the environment is protected. An important caveat is cost: the public will only support cost-effective water supply options, and water conservation and reclamation have consistently been shown to be among the most cost-effective.

THE POTENTIAL FOR ADDITIONAL WATER SUPPLIES

There is almost no likelihood that new major water supply dams will be built in northern California. The only facility with any potential is an enlarged Shasta Dam, which in fact might have some ecological benefits if operated correctly. But the likelihood that the Bureau of Reclamation would allow the state to alter its key facility, or that northern California would permit building the project solely to benefit southern California cities seems very small. The Auburn Dam would produce so little new water that it is hardly worth discussing.

Offstream storage such as Los Banos Grandes Reservoir near Los Banos or underground storage of water in Kern County would store Delta water from wet years and make it available in dry years. There is no agreement as to how much water can safely be diverted from the Delta, even during periods of very high flow. There are also concerns about the environmental impacts, particularly of the Los Banos Grandes Reservoir.

Water storage programs in existing reservoirs may be possible on the Colorado River, where unused storage can be used in water banking programs.

Water conservation can produce major savings as compared to the level of demand that would occur without conservation. New water can be provided both by installing water conserving devices and by promoting water-saving landscapes in cities. Irrigation savings can also be large, as demonstrated by the more than 400,000 acre-feet of savings possible in the Imperial Irrigation District. Wastewater reclamation can produce large amounts of water for irrigation and industrial uses in cities and may be usable for ground water recharge if allowed by the Department of Health Services.

Desalination outside southern California is still not practical economically for any large-scale uses. The costs are many times more than for any other source of water, and the energy needed to convert large amounts of sea water into usable supplies would greatly increase the state's energy consumption.

If the cities decide that conservation, reclamation, off-stream storage and water banking are not enough to meet their growing needs, there is another alternative available that is being used throughout the West. The cities can buy water from irrigators. These purchases are hard to arrange due to suspicions left over from the Owens Valley purchases and can cause environmental damage. But the pipelines are in place to move purchased water. All that is lacking is the agreement by the cities that farm water is their next major new source of supply.

There are many places that have a large supply of water being used to grow low-value crops. DWR is negotiating to buy Sherman Island in the Delta so that water from Oroville Dam will not have to be used to meet agricultural water quality standards to irrigate the island. Several agencies have purchased water from the Yuba County Water Agency, although these purchases have caused environmental damage and could cause even more in the future. (The revenue from the sales could be used to build destructive new dams.) Throughout Colorado, Nevada, Arizona and other states, cities are buying farms to obtain water rights. Clearly, this trend is heading in the direction of California.

Where are the best places to buy farm water? Where it is used on low-value crops and there is a way to get it to the cities. In the Sacramento Valley, up to 3 million acre-feet of water is used to grow rice, a water-intensive crop which would not even be grown without federal subsidies. The rice water could be allowed to flow down the Sacramento River, enhancing the fisheries there and could be used to increase fresh water outflow to the Bay and to meet SWP needs. Some of the rice water would have to be used to create new wetlands managed exclusively for waterflow, since the rice lands provide important duck habitat today.

Low-value crops grown in the Modesto and Turlock irrigation districts could be replaced by water purchased by San Francisco, and some of the water could enhance the San Joaquin River, with the rest filling San Francisco's pipelines. Another possible purchase would be part of the 3 million acre-feet of irrigation water used in the Imperial Valley, which could easily be transferred to the populated coastal plain of southern California at great financial benefit to the Imperial Valley farmers.

WILL THERE BE WATER CONSENSUS?

To achieve consensus, there must be something gained by all parties. The cities need more and better quality water. The environmentalists want to restore the Bay, Delta and their tributary rivers. But most farmers don't have urgent water needs. Some might join an urban-environmental alliance to obtain water to meet their special needs (salinity reduction, ground water overdraft, etc.). But most are happy with the way things are and are not politically ready to agree to the types of water sales which would make the cities whole.

Water is the most controversial natural resource issue in California. The 1982 vote on the Peripheral Canal produced margins of up to 97-3 in some northern California counties, reminiscent of the good old days in Bulgaria. Faced with those statistics, only a rash politician would try to impose a water solution on northern California against its will. There are many politicians in northern California who would welcome a water solution. But there are also many whose careers are linked to staunch opposition to any new water facilities or exports and who would welcome the opportunity to make political mileage out of a new water fight.

Here is an outline to solve the water problem. First, northern California must be conceded its greatest political demand. The amount of water flowing into San Francisco Bay must not be further reduced. The biological justification of this demand is in dispute but it is an undeniable political reality. Agreeing to this demand will not cost the state or federal water projects much water, for the simple reason that there is very little water left in the system which is available for export in any case.

Making this concession means that the cities will be forced to maximize conservation, reclamation and offstream storage for much of their new supplies. The rest must come from agriculture. Does this mean that irrigation has a dim future in California? Hardly. Each 1 percent of the existing irrigation supply would serve nearly 2 million new people. With stringent conservation and reclamation, perhaps 3 million people could be served. The low-value crops that would be given up would hardly be missed in the giant California farm economy.

What would the cities want in return for this concession? They want to construct a water pipeline around the Delta which would greatly increase the quality of exported water and provide greater security against floods and earthquakes. Such a pipeline also has the potential to relieve serious fish diversion and migration problems in the delta.

How would the environment benefit? The cities (and the state's general fund) would provide new water for fisheries from any construction of offstream storage south of the Delta. Much of the Delta's low-value cropland would be converted to wildlife habitat, saving water for the SWP and providing substantial new wetlands and wildlife habitat. The cities would also have to agree to fund a major new program of upstream fish and wildlife enhancement, so that the great fisheries of the Sacramento and San Joaquin rivers could be at least partially restored. Water conservation and reclamation would have to be integral parts of the cities' water development program. Any water quality pipeline would have to be operated to enhance the Delta fisheries. For each gallon of Sacramento Valley irrigation water exported, a gallon would have to go to increased outflow into San Francisco Bay in order to enhance the estuarine ecosystem.

Such a grand compromise would mean a statement by the Legislature and the governor, ratified by the voting public, that the era of expansion of irrigation in California has come to an end, and that in fact irrigation will begin to contract. While individual irrigators will benefit handsomely due to water sales, the overall power of agriculture will decline. (Of course, it is already declining due to conversion of agricultural lands to residential purposes.)

The Legislature represents a population that is more than 90 percent urban and sympathetic to the environment. An urban-environmental alliance, supported by the governor, would have great power and credibility. But the ability of farmers to control urban legislators should not be underestimated. Not only is there general sympathy with the growers, but farmers can be among the largest contributors, and that voice is still heard in the Legislature above all others. This is why it is important that at least some segments of agriculture, especially in the San Joaquin Valley, support the plan.

Gubernatorial leadership is a tremendously potent force. But the danger of being simultaneously attacked by Bay Area politicians and at least part of the powerful farm lobby may make the governor wonder if it is worth the price. However, if sufficiently large segments of the urban, agricultural and environmental communities can agree on an outline of reforms, a water package may become feasible.

THE NEED FOR CONSENSUS IN CALIFORNIA

Gloria Anderson

Group discussion/consensus is the technique most often used in the League of Women Voters for reaching member agreement on issues we study. It is a process whereby members participate in group discussion of an issue. The agreement (consensus) reached by members through group discussion is not a simple majority, nor is it unanimity; rather, it is the overall sense of the group as expressed through the exchange of ideas and opinions.

We believe that a consensus-building process can be adapted for use in discussion by groups with many different points of view. We have participated in efforts to reach agreement through consensus on a variety of issues, including water. This chapter focuses on water issues groups in which we have taken part and a perspective on what elements are essential to consensus-building efforts.

COORDINATED OPERATION AGREEMENT (COA) - 1986

The signing of the Coordinated Operation Agreement in 1986 broke a decades-long stalemate which had existed regarding

Gloria Anderson is natural resources director for the League of Women Voters (California) and a member of the Water Education Foundation's board of directors. She has served on various subcommittees of Southern California Area Governments (SCAG) and involved in state legislation in the areas of water, air and toxics.

operations of the state and federal water projects in California. The League was asked to be a part of a broad-based group which examined the COA. The group included representatives from environmental interests, state water contractors and Central Valley contractors who shared a long-term interest and expertise in water issues. Although those who participated in the process had different perspectives, they learned to understand those differences and came to trust each other as the result of their collaboration on this specific task.

Significantly, the talks took place in a non-crisis atmosphere, since 1986 was a wet year. The process was slow, but those involved acknowledged the complexity of the issues under discussion and the need to build understanding and respect for different points of view. Participants were committed to taking the time necessary to settle differences and reach agreement. They agreed that this approach would be more satisfactory than trying to find a solution in the political arena where it is difficult, if not impossible, to reach agreement that satisfies all interested parties.

Essential to the success of the process was a facilitator who understood essential points of agreement and disagreement, who knew the participants and helped them to come up with ways to address the differences which existed between them.

Because the COA was based on complicated water rights and had been negotiated by attorneys, the group recognized that changing the agreement might cause the whole process to unravel. Attorneys representing the federal and state contractors and the environmental interest helped the group to work out an agreement acceptable to all concerned. In the end, it was agreed that the COA should be left intact, but that sections should be added to the authorizing legislation to address concerns of the contractors and the environmentalists. This agreement among the concerned parties was important for getting congressional approval of the legislation.

Honesty in the negotiations was very important. The motives (which reflected the interests each was protecting or defending) of the participants were laid on the table at the beginning of the process, but it still took time to build trust. The idea of compromise had to be accepted since it was not the usual way these groups had dealt with each other.

Progress was also slow because the participants had to report back to the groups they represented for endorsement of anything agreed on by the consensus group. This ensured that the agreement was acceptable to all concerned parties.

The process resulted in all parties gaining something they did not have before the discussions took place, which was the incentive for participation. An additional benefit is that the trust and respect the participants built during their association on this issue has extended to work on other issues.

SAN JOAQUIN VALLEY DRAINAGE PROJECT - 1987

The process used by the San Joaquin Valley Drainage Project Citizens Advisory Committee enabled a diverse group of participants to work together effectively. The committee still meets and is working on an implementation plan based on the recommendations adopted by the drainage project in September 1990.

The committee was formed in 1987 and was to complete its work in two and a half years. It originally consisted of six members from the valley farming interests and six from the environmental/public interest groups, including a League representative. The committee's first task, which took several months, was to agree on two additional members. Next, rules were adopted, including the requirement that decisions or recommendations needed approval of at least three-fourths of the members; it was believed that a bare majority could not put forth recommendations of substance.

The hardest task was agreeing on a scope of work for the committee. Valley interests strongly endorsed analyzing how to construct a drain to the Delta or the ocean to carry away and dispose of drainage wastes containing salts. This idea was anathema to environmentalists. After much discussion, agricultural representatives agreed to focus on in-valley solutions for a limited period of time (two years) as a first step toward solving the San Joaquin Valley's drainage problems. With this breakthrough, work proceeded much more quickly, ably led by a chair from one interest group and vice chair from the other interest group.

Although the committee concentrated on first steps to be taken to solve a many-faceted problem, the members ability to work together is a hopeful sign that it may be possible to proceed on a step-by-step basis toward solving the valley's drainage problem.

STATE WATER CONSERVATION COALITION (SWCC) - 1989

Shortly after the Draft Salinity Plan was withdrawn and workgroups were formed by the Department of Water Resources to provide input to the State Water Resources Control Board, two groups, under the leadership of the State Water Conservation Coalition (SWCC), began meeting to try to work out an agreement on water conservation which could be implemented statewide. The SWCC brought together groups from northern and southern California in a consensus-building process. Subcommittees, called task forces, were formed to deal with various aspects of conservation: urban conservation, agricultural conservation, voluntary transfers and marketing, and reclamation. By the summer of 1991, agreement had been reached on urban water conservation and on reclamation.

The Urban Water Conservation Memorandum of Understanding (MOU) is the result of a cooperative effort between urban water agencies and public interest/environmental groups. The progress made by the urban conservation group was slow, partly because participants had to take back changes and modifications to their respective groups. A very important ingredient was the commitment of all concerned to make the agreement work. There were also legal questions to be resolved, as well as definitions and assumptions to be agreed upon. It took some time to reach agreement on the Best Management Practices (BMPs) approach as a possible formula that both sides could support, but progress was made because both groups saw the value of the end product, even though their motives were different.

More than a dozen drafts were worked on before the final form was put out for endorsement by the groups involved in the process. The League and environmental groups coordinated the "environmental" response to the draft. The question of where the conserved water would go is a major issue that has not been resolved in the MOU. Both sides agreed that nothing in the MOU precludes any group from arguing before the State Water Resources Control Board on how much water is needed for the San Francisco Bay and Sacramento-San Joaquin Delta.

A great deal of time was spent on the body of the MOU but considerable effort was expended in defining the BMPs, agreeing on the implementation schedule and establishing the assumptions for the savings for each BMP that are part of the agreement.

As far as the League and environmental groups are concerned, an important part of the agreement is the commitment by signatory urban water agencies to fund and participate in an ongoing process for studying potential BMPs and implementing them if they meet the economic criteria in the MOU. Another important feature is the council created by the agreement to monitor implementation of the MOU. All signatories have a voting seat on the council and a weighted voting system gives the public interest/environmental groups an equal say with urban water agencies in deciding when to implement new BMPs in updating the assumptions for water savings. Equity is an important part of any agreement that must satisfy a variety of interests.

It has taken longer for the Agricultural Water Conservation Task Force to build in understanding of each side's interests than for the urban task force, whose members shared a more common view of the situation. One of the problems for the agricultural task force has been the makeup of the committee. The League had been the only nonagricultural representative on it. A problem developed when environmental groups began attending meetings of the SWCC to suggest changes to the task force's document.

Although they had been following the process, the environmentalists were perceived by some SWCC members as "Johnny come-latelys," upsetting the process with a long list of suggested changes. Acceptance of their ideas has perhaps taken longer than if they had been directly involved earlier in the process. It has taken time to break down the barriers of the usually adversarial relations between environmentalists and other interests. Gaining an understanding of each other's point of view has been difficult, but it is not impossible.

None of this progress has been accomplished without a substantial commitment of time and money on the part of all concerned. It is difficult for groups with limited resources (i.e., most volunteer organizations) to participate in such a sustained effort. Another important factor is that the travel expenses have been reimbursed by the coalition, which has been able to secure grants to support the effort.

THE THREE-WAY NEGOTIATIONS - 1990

The League is also participating in a consensus effort known as the Three-Way Water Agreement Process. Representatives of major urban and agricultural water agencies and environmental organizations are engaged in a series of discussions in an effort to reach agreement on California's major water management issues that have so far defied solution. From the League's perspective, these discussions have been important because they involve major players whose organizations and interests have shaped the state's water policy for many years.

Environmental, urban, agricultural and other interests are working to create an agreement which will meet the goals and interests of all sides and to ensure the existence of a political and regulatory atmosphere wherein all sides feel secure that the agreement will protect them in the future. Several elements of the agreement are being developed sequentially, but with all participants agreeing that no element will stand alone. The elements will be interdependent and will comprise a package agreement. In addition, the parties may agree to jointly pursue other specific projects.

Each group is equally represented: one-third urban, one-third agriculture, one-third environment. Between meetings of all Three-Way participants, called plenary sessions, a steering committee comprised of six members from each group has functioned as the chief negotiating team. Each major group has been caucusing between both the plenary sessions and the steering committee meetings in order to develop a unified approach to the negotiations. The caucuses also allow the larger group to give direction to the steering committee and to seek input from the larger community outside the plenary delegation. In addition, subcommittees have been formed to discuss major areas and any delegate, as well as consultants who have needed expertise, may participate.

To date, the group has operated without a neutral facilitator, but each group has contributed a staff person to a three-person team that coordinates the work of the steering committee and the subcommittees. They also facilitate the meetings. In the future, a neutral facilitator and additional technical expertise may be needed to help resolve the more difficult issues.

Although the delegates could be characterized as professionals with the necessary expertise to fashion innovative and substantive solutions to water management, any package agreement must be subjected to public scrutiny and input from more diverse interests than are now at the table. The necessity for a broad base of support has been recognized by all groups, and the delegates have agreed that a small delegation from the steering committee should communicate progress to the governor, the speaker of the Assembly and the president of the Senate.

Additionally, the environmental caucus has undertaken an effort to reach out and involve representatives of ethnically diverse communities in the process. Members of ethnic groups have been invited to meetings held before each plenary session and efforts to involve these groups will continue. The caucus has also made efforts to balance its delegation geographically.

Besides finding solutions to long-standing water management problems, the group will have to address the best method for ensuring the public input necessary for any far-reaching agreement to be put in place.

CALIFORNIANS FOR WATER - 1991

In June 1991, approximately 100 individuals gathered in Santa Cruz at the invitation of a group called Californians for Water (CFW). Those invited included not only representatives of traditional water interests, but also business, labor and ethnic communities. At the initial meeting, those attending decided that the group could play a useful role in bringing together diverse interests to agree on what should be included in a water policy for California. However, they were concerned that unless more environmentalists can be persuaded to participate in CFW, it may not be effective in building consensus that will satisfy all interests. As a result, a concerted effort is being made to get more participation by environmental groups.

There was also discussion about the role of CFW in relation to other consensus-building efforts and whether it was necessary to have another group working on water policy. Participants agreed that the work of other groups should be incorporated.

Unlike some of the other efforts, this meeting was professionally facilitated. One advantage of this approach is that a lot more can be accomplished in a shorter time. The organizers also attempted to develop a sense of togetherness or group identity in the short time of the conference, and the setting helped to build a feeling of good will.

In its early stages, CFW holds some promise for incorporating and building on the work of other consensus groups and is bringing into the process a broader-based group than has been previously involved, notably the business community, labor and ethnic groups.

CONCLUSION

Some may question the need for all the current consensus-building efforts, but considering the complexity and diversity of California, perhaps there is a place for all. Everyone agrees that the status quo is not satisfactory and that the water wars must end for the good of California. However, a time may come when representatives of each effort should meet to work on lasting solutions to California's water problems.

The value of the consensus process is that mutual gains are more likely to result than under the adversarial approach which usually results in one side winning at the expense of the other side. Although all parties involved may not get everything they want, they have a better chance of getting something they can live with than with the more contentious approach.

Based on an assessment of these efforts, it would seem that to be successful, the process needs:

* Honesty—trust can't be established without it.
* Commitment of the participants to reach agreement—get it in the beginning, or there's no sense proceeding.
* Willingness to understand other points of view.
* Respect for the opinions of others.
* Willingness to compromise—recognition that half a loaf is better than nothing.
* Fair play, cooperative spirit.
* Focus on *interests*, not positions—sticking to a position means no concessions, no compromising; protecting interests allows compromise.
* Basic knowledge of issues, common understanding of facts.
* Definition of problems, recognition of obstacles to solution.

To be effective, a group's facilitator must be chosen carefully. Ideally, the individual should be a neutral party with discussion-leading skills. And unless meetings are facilitated professionally, participants should recognize that the process may take more time than people are willing or able to commit. Care should also go into selecting the individuals who participate in consensus-building efforts. They should be committed to working with the group to reach agreement on the issue. Creative thinkers are especially desirable in a consensus-building group.

There is a difference of opinion about what subjects should be discussed. Perhaps the approach should be to tackle the issues on which agreement may be possible (the "easy" issues), and then, after trust and a working relationship have been established, it may be possible to go on to the harder issues. There may be some subjects on which there could never be agreement—the Peripheral Canal, for example—and so may not be appropriate for discussion. In that case, it may be better to agree to discuss a more general subject, such as facilities, and then try to reach agreement on what facilities would be acceptable.

The League's experience working with various consensus groups has led us to believe that, ultimately, these voluntary efforts may be successful because those who are involved have recognized the need to find mutually acceptable solutions to old problems using a new approach. There is still much work to be done, but progress is being made. Warring factions are learning to work together and we are optimistic that a lasting agreement can be reached on water policy in California in this decade.

Environmental groups want to see more water released to protect fish such as these spawn-bound wild steelhead in the South Fork Trinity River. Environmentalists believe the water projects are responsible for the destruction of the fisheries. Photo credit: California Trout Inc.

AN OVERVIEW OF THE THREE-WAY PROCESS

David Fullerton

For the first time in California history, key members of the environmental, urban and agricultural communities are meeting in a serious attempt to agree on how California should manage its water into the 21st century.

The discussions, known as the Three-Way Water Agreement Process, stem from the dissatisfaction felt by all those interested in a rational water policy for California. Decades of legal and political struggle have achieved little, except to leave the environmental and urban and agricultural supplies in an increasingly precarious position. All sides now agree that a non-adversarial approach to water policy could lead to significant benefits for all.

In contrast to the traditional wisdom, the Three-Way Process is ad hoc, organized by the participants on an informal basis. The various sides have provided their own staffing. The level of importance attached to these discussions may be gauged by the breadth of participation and, even more importantly, by the stature of the participants within their communities. The governor, key members of the state and federal legislature, and state and federal agency officials have all expressed a keen interest in the process and offered their support to make it successful.

David Fullerton is a resource scientist with the Natural Heritage Institute, and the chair of the Sierra Club of Northern California Water Committee.

The future of water policy in the state may well depend upon the success or failure of the Three-Way Process. Either we will construct a new water resource management system in which the legitimate needs of all water users are enhanced and protected, or we will revert to the internecine warfare of the past few decades, in which all interests suffer from the lack of a rational system of water management.

THE WATER POLICY IMPASSE: AN ENVIRONMENTAL PERSPECTIVE

Fear drives the conflict over water policy in California. None of the three active protagonists—environmentalists, urban agencies and agriculture—have faith that their interests will be adequately considered in the future. Not trusting in the future, not trusting in their collective ability to construct a system in which the needs of individual interests will continue to be satisfied, they fight each battle as if it were the last and insist that their needs from now to doomsday be guaranteed as a precondition of consensus. California water policy has become nothing less than trench warfare and woe be it to anyone caught in the cross fire.

From an environmental point of view, trench warfare is preferable to outright defeat. Environmentalists can point to a long string of injuries inflicted upon our lakes, streams, rivers and estuaries over the last century. Until the 1970s, despite periodic fights, water development was essentially unchecked. But with the rise of the environmental movement, the paucity of good water development sites and budgetary problems, the balance tipped against development. Indeed, many reacted with horror at what we had done to our fish and wildlife, to our wetlands and to our free-flowing rivers. Most environmentalists concluded that, in our pursuit of the benefits of water development, we have inflicted an unreasonable amount of damage on the environment and thus, not only is major new development unreasonable, but restoration and remediation of past damage is a prerequisite for any discussion of additional agricultural and urban demands.

Unfortunately, environmental obstruction of new water development has not translated into significant environmental restoration. Instead, environmental efforts to allocate more water for environmental purposes and to move water management patterns toward conservation, reclamation, ground water banking, the retirement of marginal land and voluntary water transfers have been obstructed. Water users fear that the dedication of large amounts of new water for environmental protection could not only complicate their efforts to expand water supplies, but could even result in absolute losses in supply. In the agricultural sector, some of these strategies could threaten local control over water supply and could have negative impacts on the rural community.

If all sides were reasonably satisfied with the status quo, then a policy impasse might be acceptable. But this is not the case. For urban and environmental interests, the status quo is clearly not acceptable. Environmentalists cannot accept the current degraded state of the San Francisco Bay-Delta Estuary, nor the San Joaquin River, nor many other degraded habitats. Urban agencies are increasingly worried about their ability to continue to provide reliable and high quality water. Agriculture might accept the status quo, but with the environment and the cities seeking changes, agriculture has been pulled into the fray in self-defense.

The result has been a maelstrom of conflict, in which no side has been able to advance its own agenda in the face of opposition from one or two of the other players. For each side, that opposition has its roots in fear about the future, fear that, in a zero-sum world, any compromise or concession only works to the advantage of the other side.

The consensus approach attempts to surmount the zero-sum philosophy, calm the fears and create solutions that leave all sides better off.

THE FAILURE OF TRADITIONAL APPROACHES

Many people in the environmental camp feel strongly that time is on their side and that inaction will force changes beneficial to their interest. Many environmentalists feel that if urban agencies are blocked from all increased diversions from the environment, then urban agencies will pursue more "enlightened" water management. Moreover, they feel that their judicial and political positions will become stronger over time.

Agricultural, urban and environmental groups frequently attempt to negotiate small, self-contained consensus agreements. Regulatory and resource agencies frequently attempt to respond to their mandate (to provide water and to protect the environment) in a step-by-step fashion. These agreements and proposals seek to provide benefits to everyone, or at least to avoid harm to anyone.

Unfortunately, very few actions can be considered in isolation from the broader concerns of the various interests. Thus, all proposals to increase Delta transfers—even proposals which could provide local environmental benefits—rouse environmental opposition since restoration of the San Francisco Bay-Delta Estuary has not been made part of the package. When environmentalists do not trust the political and regulatory system to restore and maintain the environment, incremental diversions merely appear to lock up more water in consumptive uses and reduce the incentive of agricultural and urban interests to accept environmental restoration.

Similarly, proposals to increase flows for the protection of the San Francisco Bay-Delta Estuary will presumably be opposed by urban and agricultural interests. After all, without assurances that future demands can be met, water users have little to gain and a lot to lose from increased flows dedicated to environmental protection.

FUNDAMENTAL REORIENTATION BY CONSENSUS

Incrementalism can help in isolated instances, but the major changes needed to restore the water environment, while protecting the urban and agricultural interests, cannot be made piecemeal. When important interests are ignored, the result is conflict, not resolution. A global package agreement is needed which both responds to the goals of all sides <u>and</u> allows each of them to trust in the future. Only in this way will we blunt the inclination to torpedo every individual proposal.

Such a solution would protect the water supply, quality and reliability needs of urban interests, protect the financial and social health of our farm system, allow major restoration of the environment, and create a political and regulatory atmosphere in which all sides can feel secure.

Satisfaction of near-term goals is the easier requirement. There is little question that we could devise a set of facilities (e.g., Delta transfer facilities, in-Delta and south-of-Delta storage, expanded cross valley canal) and operating criteria (e.g., flow, temperature and pumping standards for the Delta and its tributaries) that would greatly improve the riverine and estuarine environment, and provide reliable and high quality urban supplies without major harm to the environment, agriculture or urban users. *This is not and has never been the core issue.*

The nub is simply this: what happens in twenty or thirty years if growing cities need more water? Environmentalists fear that the very facilities used to improve the environment now (particularly increased Delta transfer capacity) will be used later to cause even more environmental damage than has already occurred—for example, destruction of the estuary *and* destruction of the northern rivers. Thus, for environmentalists, guarantees that present agreements will not lead to future disaster are a precondition to discussions over facilities.

Similarly, agricultural interests are concerned lest the growing demand in the cities be quenched at their expense, with ever-increasing water transfers out of agriculture leading inexorably towards another Owens Valley in the Central Valley. If urban areas are to be allowed access to agricultural water, agriculture will want assurances that the rural areas of the state will not simply be bought out or bullied by the richer coastal cities. This fear underlies the continued agricultural suspicion of ag/urban entanglements such as water transfer agreements and large-scale conjunctive use projects.

In both the environmental and agricultural cases, basic fears must be calmed before rational discussion of solutions is even possible. For environmentalists, guarantees must be based upon real changes in how we manage water and upon assurances that the agreement will not be vulnerable to the political process. Agriculture is concerned that such a shift could harm the rural economy and culture. The solution must provide confidence that the rural community retains its right of "self determination."

Finally, urban agencies would need assurances that the quality, quantity and reliability of their water supplies will not be threatened in the future, even with the continuation of urban growth. To a large extent, once environmental and agricultural concerns are dealt with, these urban goals are readily obtained. Indeed, the environmental and agricultural need for guarantees is predicated on the notion that the cities, once mobilized, may be able to overcome all opposition. The key is to insist that their approach to obtaining water should complement rather than conflict with environmental and agricultural interests.

THE EVOLUTION OF THE THREE-WAY PROCESS

Bilateral Discussions

The Three-Way Process evolved out of two separate bilateral discussions, one between urban water agency managers and agricultural water district managers, the other between urban water managers and environmental leaders. The ag/urban meetings have been labelled the Pardee group and the environmental/urban meetings have been labelled the Hetch Hetchy group, after the initial locations of the meetings. The Pardee group began meeting in late 1989 and the Hetch Hetchy group in mid-1990.

The Pardee group inititally focused on the question of agricultural-to-urban water transfers. Attempts were made to identify and quantify water potentially available for transfer and to understand the impediments to such transfers. Ultimately, the group concluded that, unless the problem of Delta transfer and other basic water policy issues are resolved, the potential for voluntary water transfers are fairly limited. The Pardee group comprised about 20 water managers and was staffed by Lyle Hoag, executive director of California Urban Water Agencies (CUWA), Steve Hall, executive director of California Farm Water Coalition (CFWA), and B.J. Miller, consulting engineer.

The Hetch Hetchy group began by examining the goals of environmental and urban water organizations for areas of common interest and possible cooperation. Topics of discussion included the need for environmental enhancement, high quality water supply and reliable urban water supplies. Discussions were then begun on ways to simultaneously achieve the goals of the environmental groups and urban water agencies. The Hetch Hetchy group was staffed by Lyle Hoag and David Fullerton of the Natural Heritage Institute.

The Hetch Hetchy discussions on the prospects for a mutually beneficial program were quite fruitful and provided the basic underpinnings of the Three-Way Process. In essence, environmentalists required three general elements to enter into a consensus agreement on water management:

* Immediate environmental benefits, particularly instream flow enhancements and habitat improvements.

* A process to improve upon those benefits with time.

* The creation of a legal, institutional management structure which would guarantee that environmental benefits would be retained over time. A strong preference was expressed for a water management reorientation which would steer water users away from the environment and toward such approaches as conservation, reclamation (recycling) and water transfer.

Urban water managers felt that any agreement must include:

* Assurances that urban agencies will be able to obtain water supplies of high reliability and quality in the future. A strong belief was expressed that environmental and urban goals could not be reconciled without additional Delta water transfer facilities. Many felt that, of the Delta transfer options, some form of isolated transfer was clearly superior because of drinking water quality degradation and other risks associated with the Delta.

Three-Way Discussions Begin

In December 1990, the Hetch Hetchy group, at the request of the Pardee group, agreed to explore the possibility of discussions involving all three interests. A steering committee was formed which included the staffs of the three groups, as well as other members of the delegations, for a total of twelve people. Environmental interests were initially skeptical that agricultural representatives would be willing to discuss the broad changes they had in mind. In fact, the discussions were very constructive and it rapidly became clear to all that a far-reaching agreement which would satisfy the three interests was a possibility. As articulated, agricultural managers felt that any agreement must include:

* Assurances that farmers and agricultural districts would not lose control over their water, that average agricultural production would not diminish and that the rural communities would not suffer socioeconomic disruption.

At a large meeting on Jan. 11, 1991, the two sets of discussions were formally merged into what has become known as the Three-Way Water Agreement Process. Approximately 35 people attended this meeting. At the plenary meeting, the steering committee and staff presented their recommendations for the future direction of the discussions.

The key approach endorsed by the entire group of delegates was that of consensus based upon a major, indivisible package agreement. In such a package, the parties would strive to create an agreement which provides benefits for each side overall. However, individual elements of the package would have no meaning in isolation.

The plenary group also endorsed, in concept, a package containing these general elements:

* Bay-Delta environmental protections;
* Wildlife habitat enhancement, including wetlands;
* Water management (e.g., conjunctive use, transfers, conservation, reclamation);
* Necessary water storage, conveyance and management facilities;

* Measures to address regulatory constraints on needed facilities.

By consensus, the parties agreed to focus initially on the question of Bay-Delta environmental guarantees, based upon the assumption that environmentalists would not be willing to discuss water transfer facilities unless they felt comfortable with the guarantees section of the package.

ORGANIZATION

The initial organizational structure has been retained with a few modifications. The plenary group has been expanded to 60 people, 20 delegates from each of the three groups. The steering committee has been expanded to 18 members.

A plenary session is expected every two to three months. The steering committee meets more frequently, every two to three weeks. The steering committee and its subcommittees are the working policy core of the consensus effort. The four staff members of the Pardee and Hetch Hetchy groups continue to coordinate the work.

PROGRESS OF THE DISCUSSIONS

The first substantive topic of discussion for the steering committee and its subcommittees has been the issue of adequate environmental guarantees. Unless credible guarantees can be constructed, environmentalists will probably not be able to support any agreement which involves additional Delta transfer.

Conversely, if such guarantees can be constructed, the question of Delta transfer should become less controversial. Greg Thomas of the Natural Heritage Institute has taken a lead on this issue as convener of the environmental guarantees subcommittee. The subcommittee has now focused its attention on a guarantees package consisting of an environmental water agency, vested with water supplies, and having a degree of operational control over the state and federal water projects. The arrangement would be cemented by a combination of state and federal legislation and private contracts.

Another subcommittee has been formed to discuss the question of voluntary water transfers (where transfers could include numerous types of arrangements, from conservation to conjunctive use to land retirement). The committee is focusing on ways to rationalize the transfer of water in such a way that agricultural interests feel that agriculture and the rural community are secure enough to allow the widespread intrusion of ag/urban arrangements, while cities feel that the transfer system will be able to respond to their needs. Work to date has centered on creating a California water exchange to facilitate and manage short-term water transfers and to ensure an orderly and responsible market.

Future work will focus on filling out the other parts of the framework of the agreement. A subcommittee is now forming to discuss how wetland habitat enhancement could be integrated into the process.

Finally, the ability of the existing water supply system to provide for all the competing water supply needs will be evaluated, as well as options for the enhancements possible through the construction of various facilities, including water banking, surface storage, and water transfer facilities.

RESOLUTION OF ENVIRONMENTAL ISSUES IN THE ENVIRONMENTAL AGE

David A. Vogel

THE PROBLEM

"Good God, you folks aren't building nuclear warheads! Why are you all so paranoid? You're *only* working on fish and wildlife problems." The well-known environmental author concluded his presentation to aspiring natural resource leaders and left the audience with some individuals smiling and nodding in agreement, some confused at his apparent irreverence and disregard for the critical importance of protecting natural resources and some outright angry at traitorous statements in his speech. I'll admit, I chuckled. Not directly because of his statements, but rather because I was reminded of similar statements my father, a retired engineer who worked on the design of U.S. weaponry, had espoused to me during my 14-year career with the U.S. Fish and Wildlife Service. Probably everyone there agreed: for someone whose life is dedicated to natural resource protection, it's difficult to convey the importance of fish

Dave Vogel is a senior fisheries biologist with CH2M Hill, an environmental engineering consulting firm. During his 14 years with the U.S. Fish and Wildlife Service, he designed and conducted research projects on Central Valley salmon populations and developed fishery resource restoration programs.

and wildlife in comparison to national security and the potential for global annihilation through thermonuclear conflict.

Most of the future natural resource leaders attending this first annual National Fish and Wildlife Foundation program believed they were in training to develop the knowledge and skills for future "warfare" on the environmental front. The enemy was clear: anyone or any entity attempting to destroy fish and wildlife resources and their habitat through land and water development activities. At the onset of the training program, most believed they would become adept at hurtling headlong into future fracases, armed with as-yet-unknown "weapons" to beat back the forces intent on environmental destruction.

After some weeks of formal training and hearing speeches from a wide variety of non-governmental experts proficient in resolving natural resource conflicts, the words "consensus building," "negotiation," "mediation," "balanced approach" and "problem resolution" had worn thin on some trainees. To them it appeared that this program was nothing more than bureaucracy's attempt to clone them into faceless resource administrators hidden in obscure national, regional and state offices with the skills to safely sidestep the *real* environmental issues and allow the nation's fish and wildlife populations to relentlessly decline until they could slip comfortably into retirement and let someone else worry about the difficult problems. For these people, the proper approach was simply a matter of *strictly* enforcing the mandates of Congress, such as the Endangered Species Act and the Clean Water Act, and "shut down" any developer whose greedy, self-serving intents were deemed incompatible with the nation's natural resources. If it took direct warfare or indirect subterfuge tactics to protect the environment, then so be it. These folks knew of numerous examples of such "successful" approaches throughout the country where water development was halted dead in its tracks.

However, for a small group of others in attendance, a spark of enlightenment began to glow and an enthusiasm for a fresh approach to resource protection was fanned into a flame of hot intensity that they had not known since their early days of biological field work where their direct contact with fish and wildlife first occurred on a professional basis. It was during these early years when they initially became obsessed with concern over the nation's declining fish and wildlife. These individuals signed up for the National Fish and Wildlife Foundation's training because they had come to realize that, in many instances, the confrontational approach to resource protection had numerous failures and was steadily establishing a foreboding harbinger of major future losses on environmental issues. There were indications that such environmental protection tactics were beginning to wane among the populace despite periodic dramatic and newsworthy apparent successes. They were concerned that when the pendulum swings back again, the necessary foundations for environmental protection will not be established to prevent it from swinging too far in the opposite direction. Most of all, these individuals were deeply concerned that present tactics using confrontation were beginning to have a subtle, insidious, long-term adverse effect on fish and wildlife resources themselves. It seemed that, in many cases, those resources could not be protected in spite of themselves because of the very mechanisms and strategies being employed to supposedly save those resources. Increased attention was being focused on the act of fighting battles rather than solving environmental problems.

IDEALISM VERSUS PRAGMATISM

In an ideal world it's easy to imagine a pristine environment free of all the associated adverse impacts humans have created on the world. Clear, free-flowing rivers and vast marshlands with teeming fish and wildlife can be easily visualized. Such an emotionally and aesthetically appealing perspective is attractive to nearly everyone in California; many believe that such an ecological utopia would ease, if not cure, many of society's ailments.

Conversely, it also takes very little effort to envision a metropolitan sprawl of buildings, parking lots, freeways and homes with no place available for cohabitation by fish and wildlife. In this regard, the pointed question, "What do you want—people or fish?!" has often been asked. Emphasizing this problem and with bitter pragmatic reality as his justification, an acquaintance presently working for a natural resource agency in California once told me: "My job is simply to monitor the decline of California's natural resources. Because we cannot control growth, it's hopeless to expect [that] the fish and wildlife populations can ever be restored. At best, we can only slow their rate of decline."

Extreme idealism or pragmatism are obviously not the philosophies needed to achieve consensus on California's water and environmental issues. Somewhere in between, in an as-yet-undefined middle ground, is the answer. The consensus-building process is the most appropriate mechanism available to develop the truly balanced approach to resolving the resource conflicts.

SCIENCE VERSUS POLITICS

Many modern-day natural resource managers and scientists firmly believe that the cause of environmental degradation in California is attributable to politics overriding the scientific evidence which would have avoided adverse impacts. In other words, they state, "If only the decision-makers had listened to the environmental scientists. . . we would not be in this mess today." The National Fish and Wildlife Foundation recognized this dilemma and addressed it as follows:

> Answers to the problems that face the environment today clearly require scientifically sound solutions. Obstacles to solutions, however, are not exclusively scientific, but are social, economic, and political as well. Many proposals that are biologically or environmentally "correct" are never implemented because their proponents fail to influence decisions. It is necessary, therefore, to complement plans for technical solutions with plans for "political" solutions—plans that reconcile the many different and opposing interests that come into play on most environmental policies.

GOVERNMENT AGENCY POLICIES AND POSITIONS

In many instances, a major barrier to achieving consensus on water and environmental conflicts in California are the formal policies and positions of government agencies. Although guiding policies are necessary for agencies to clearly define their missions in the overall scheme of things, if they are improperly worded, these elements can create impasses to developing a consensus on water policy issues. Resource agency staff have used such agency policies and positions on numerous occasions as "shields" against moving toward the consensus-building process. In a hypothetical example, an agency representative could easily refer to an agency document and state: "I have no alternative in this issue. My agency has the formally-stated position that no more water withdrawals from this river should occur. Therefore, for me or anyone in my agency to develop a consensus on increasing this proposed riverine diversion would be inconsistent with our position and I would be negligent in my duties to the agency." In this example, the discussion should focus on preventing destruction of the resource, not on stopping water development; the two are not necessarily mutually exclusive. While working with the U.S. Fish and Wildlife Service, a close co-worker once said: "Stating agency policy is the *easy* way out. The difficult way is to face the issue head-on and resolve it to everyone's satisfaction."

PROBLEM IDENTIFICATION

It is safe to state that developing consensus on water and environmental issues in California has not been, nor is it likely to be, easy. The reason is that environmental issues have two principal components which make it particularly difficult to apply the consensus-building process toward problem resolution. They are usually technically complex and have scientific uncertainty.

Intuitively, most people know that the first step in problem resolution is simply understanding what the problem is in the first place. However, an environmental problem is often difficult to grasp and accurately define because of insufficient scientific understanding of ecosystem mechanisms. Cause and effect relationships in the environment are usually extremely complex. Any lack of scientific knowledge severely impairs the ability to solve an environmental problem, and therefore the first step toward resolution can't be achieved. With this in mind, it is surprising that in the modern-day arena of resolving environmental problems associated with water development, not that much effort goes into *truly* understanding the problem. Sure, a lot of research is continually being conducted on resource issues, but it is often misdirected, general in nature, not *applied* research; it could be more appropriately termed "biological monitoring activities." A true scientific approach to accurately defining and understanding the problem is often not employed. As stated previously, answers to environmental problems require scientifically sound solutions.

A basic precept of scientific research is that a null hypothesis is established and then the scientist works to accept or reject that hypothesis. An example of a null hypothesis in research would be that a certain chemical has no adverse effect on fish or wildlife. The scientist then carefully designs experiments to determine whether that hypothesis should be accepted or rejected based on statistical analyses of his test results. A null hypothesis used in our judicial system is that a person is innocent until proven guilty; the jurors carefully examine the evidence to determine if there is enough evidence to accept or reject that hypothesis. Objective, unbiased scientific research is paramount to increasing our understanding of resource problems and how to resolve those problems.

Unfortunately, there are many examples where the opposite is incorrectly employed. An inherent danger in the latter approach is that a quasi-scientific method stifles the necessary insight and objectivity needed to develop a proper and complete understanding of a problem. Furthermore, if the research conducted in the latter fashion does not yield results to support the desired end-product, those results often don't see the light of day. Imagine the ramifications if our legal system was established on the basis that a person was guilty until proven innocent and *only* certain information was presented to implicate guilt.

Bits and pieces of good research cumulatively can vastly improve the level of understanding of resource problems and generate the necessary creativity and knowledge to solve the problems. The public and decision-makers need to know all the facts, not just those facts supporting one agenda. This is applicable to both pro-and anti-environmental interests. In his commencement address at UCLA in the spring of 1991, Carl Sagan perhaps said it best: ". . . it is the responsibility of scientists never to suppress knowledge, no matter how awkward that knowledge is, no matter how it may bother those in power, we are not smart enough to decide which pieces of knowledge are permissible and which are not."

Objective scientific research may reveal that a specific type of water development activity could be devastating to the environment. Assuming that the water development is necessary in the first place, better alternatives to that specific activity should be pursued. Given sufficient creativity and scientific insight, a different, more environmentally compatible approach can usually be developed. Focusing everyone's energy on developing and implementing better alternatives seems like a more appropriate use of time and resources, rather than fighting over one particular approach.

DEVELOPING SOLUTIONS

Recently, a colleague asked me, "Where have all the natural resource problem-solvers and positive thinkers gone?" He was simply voicing his frustration with the apparent immobility in developing action-oriented resolutions to environmental problems in general. The fishery resource was on a general downward spiral and it seemed to this person that no one was taking charge to aggressively reverse the decline. Everyone appeared to be squabbling over principles, philosophies and position statements, rather than rolling up their shirt-sleeves and tackling the issues with a "can-do" attitude. I think he was

144   *Water Policy in California*

partially correct; such individuals are there within the government agencies, but can be hard to find and often are not allowed to be players in conflict resolution. Those with a proactive attitude generally receive little, if any, rewards for their efforts.

A present-day problem-solver in a natural resource agency has be innovative in biological and political approaches to environmental problem resolution. In the proper atmosphere, most folks often surprise themselves with their creativity. However, the proper atmosphere for creative thinking is often diminished by the ominous specter of *taking risks*. To rank-and-file bureaucrats, risk-taking by itself is an unacceptable risk to comfortable civil service employment. To some, penalties associated with the risk of failure and assumed impacts on their careers overshadow any potential natural resource benefit; it would be simply better not to take such chances. Worse yet, their superiors may frown on such aggressive behavior. Whether real or perceived, these attitudes eventually snuff out the creativity necessary for environmental problem resolution.

Some years ago, I served on a task force to conduct an internal audit of higher-level U.S. Fish and Wildlife Service management practices in six western states. After conducting detailed interviews with a wide variety of field-level staff, one extremely interesting conclusion was unveiled. Universally, the Fish and Wildlife personnel interviewed greatly preferred higher-level management to make timely decisions, *even if that decision was wrong*, rather than have no decision made at all. These folks were tired of indecisiveness at high levels in government simply because managers were not willing to take risks in their careers. Years later, during the National Fish and Wildlife Foundation's management training, I learned that a major factor contributing to the success of Fortune 500 CEOs was their ability to make timely decisions based on calculated risks. The training stressed that, to succeed in resource protection, future natural resource managers must learn to take on more calculated risks. Indecision, by itself, was helping to destroy natural resources.

No one likes to be wrong, but everyone admires someone who admits he or she is wrong and, if necessary, rights that wrong. If a decision on water policy and the environment is made on the best available information at the time, yet that decision is ultimately revealed as incorrect, a commitment has to be made to correct it. Doing so accomplishes two things: the development of trust among all concerned and long-term protection of the environment. A commitment to correct mistakes before those mistakes are known is even more valuable. It is truly impossible to absolutely know all possible effects any particular water development project may have on the environment. But if the commitment is made to fix the problem if things go awry, it will be much easier to develop consensus on that issue. Examples of past environmental destruction which have gone uncorrected are barriers toward developing consensus on future water and environmental issues. Future processes would benefit greatly if past wrongs were amended.

An extremely useful tool for developing solutions to environmental problems is simply group brainstorming. It is only effective, though, if it occurs among a broad diversity of individuals, interest groups and disciplines. Because no one knows all the answers, group brainstorming is invaluable for bringing out fresh new perspectives which can serve as catalysts toward developing innovative approaches to problem resolution. Group brainstorming also creates a broader range of alternatives to consider than if only a limited number of people is involved.

THE CONSENSUS-BUILDING PROCESS: AN EXAMPLE THAT IS WORKING

Early in 1987, an unlikely group of diverse individuals met for the first time to initiate discussions toward the formulation of an Upper Sacramento River Fisheries and Riparian Habitat Management Plan in northern California. The unusual characteristic of this group was that the entire spectrum, from the most ardent land and water developers to environmental preservationists, was represented. The general public was also encouraged to participate. As an example of the variety of perspectives presented, at one of the first meetings one person seriously suggested that if the Sacramento River fishery resource was purposely eliminated, the conflict over water for agriculture and fish would be gone. In response, one environmentalist said "likewise for Central Valley agriculture." And so it began—the stage was set for some of the most argumentative, frustrating, sometimes unproductive, yet ultimately revealing and rewarding meetings in which I've ever been involved.

This process was established by California Senate Bill 1086. The bill authorized establishment of a group of 26 entities, each one with some stake in the development of the Sacramento River plan. Initially, I was a firm believer that this effort had a fatal flaw in that it had far too many players. However, after two years and the conclusion of the group's efforts, I knew I was wrong. It could not have succeeded to the degree that it had without the diverse composition of the team. A consensus for a Sacramento River management plan was developed because considerable effort was made to include everyone who would be necessary to implement the plan or could block the final outcome. Lines of communication were opened where none had previously existed. After decades of arguing, finger-pointing, fragmentation and inaction, a workable plan for restoration of the Sacramento River's fishery resources and riparian habitat was hammered out through the consensus-building process. Although all involved agreed that the plan was not perfect, it was a major step toward fish and wildlife restoration. However, the process is not complete: various federal legislative packages to implement the program are under consideration. Congress and the state Legislature have yet to use the same consensus-building process to compete the final phase in this massive effort.

THE FUTURE

"We need to rethink our approach...The old ways of doing things have run their course. Find new ones."—President George

Bush, May 4, 1991 Commencement Address, The University of Michigan.

This advice is particularly appropriate to the resolution of water issues in California. The old ways of dealing with California water issues are no longer appropriate in this environmental age. The issues are not static and the people and natural resources require aggressive, innovative approaches to resolving those issues. Productive group brainstorming should be greatly encouraged. Innovation among resource professionals demonstrating the creativity and resolve to tackling the issues with a "can-do," problem-solving attitude should be recognized for their accomplishments.

If nothing is done, fish and wildlife resources in California will assuredly decline, many into obscurity or extinction. Stalemating or avoiding the environmental issues can ultimately be as harmful as a direct onslaught on the resource itself. Leaders of the state have to be willing to assume the necessary political and biological risks to conclusively define the problems, develop workable solutions and achieve consensus among those concerned. If the risks fail, the necessary commitment to correct those mistakes must be made. Not easy tasks, but the only rational course of action; the resource and California cannot afford to wait.

The Suisun Marsh in the Delta provides an important resting ground on the Pacific Flyway. Agricultural interests argue that irrigated rice fields in the Sacramento Valley serve a similar purpose for migrating birds. Photo credit: Water Education Foundation.

THE ENVIRONMENTAL HERITAGE OF CALIFORNIA

J. William Yeates

Several months ago I was invited by the Contra Costa Water District to speak about Delta fisheries during a boat tour of the Sacramento-San Joaquin Delta. Driving to Concord that Saturday morning, I pondered what I would actually say and wondered who would be my audience on this boat tour. As usual, I had put off thinking about what to say until the last minute.

I am certainly no expert on Delta fisheries like Pete Chadwick or Dan Odenweller at the Department of Fish and Game. When it comes to fishing in the Delta, I am a novice— certainly Jay Sorensen, president of the California Striped Bass Association, would be a more knowledgeable spokesperson. As I pulled into the parking lot at the Concord Hilton, I was just hoping that I could get enough of a sense of the event from the other speakers so that I could prepare some spontaneous remarks.

Fortunately, I bumped into my friend Bob Bosworth. Bob Bosworth is a self-proclaimed "good old boy" whose family has been cattle ranching and timbering in Shasta County for over 150 years. But for some reason, a few years ago Cowboy Bob Bosworth decided to become a Shasta County supervisor. His election didn't shake up state politics and his public service went relatively unnoticed outside of local political circles. However,

Bill Yeates is a partner in the Sacramento law firm of Remy & Thomas. He specializes in California Environmental Quality Act (CEQA) and land use litigation. He represents a variety of non-profit environmental and business organizations.

due to his interest in the Sacramento River and his official status, he just happened to be available to serve on the Upper Sacramento River Fisheries and Riparian Habitat Advisory Council when people were drawing straws to serve on this "doomed to failure" panel.

The Upper Sacramento River Advisory Council's charge in September 1986 was to develop a comprehensive management plan for the Upper Sacramento River basin "for the protection, enhancement, and restoration of fish and riparian habitat and associated wildlife, as part of the orderly development of water resources of the Sacramento River Basin for all beneficial purposes." This *Upper Sacramento River Fisheries and Riparian Habitat Management Plan* was to be completed by Jan. 1, 1989.

The advisory council was created by the enactment of Senate Bill 1086, which had been authored by former state Sen. Jim Nielsen. The lengthiest section of Sen. Nielsen's bill was the listing of all the federal and state agencies, local supervisors, landowners, fishing organizations and environmental groups that were to be represented on the council. When state Sen. Robert Presley, chairman of the Senate Appropriations Committee, out of frustration once stated that there will come a time when every Californian will have served on some advisory board or council in his or her lifetime, he must have had the Upper Sacramento River Advisory Council in mind.

To further perpetuate the feeling among some in Sacramento (and I was one among many in this camp) that this was a bill dominated by local landowners and their elected representatives, the advisory council selected good old boy Shasta County Supervisor Bob Bosworth as its chair. The next fateful move by the council was to require that all recommendations of the advisory council be made on the basis of consensus. This assured failure, which was all right by me, since I was sure it was a stacked deck anyway. For example, there was surely no way that any representative for the commercial salmon fishermen would ever agree with the Bureau of Reclamation on programs to restore the Sacramento River. Why worry about trying to reach consensus with the Bureau—just try to imagine the local landowners reaching agreement with the Sacramento River Preservation Trust!

For two and a half years, Bob Bosworth chaired this advisory council, but surprisingly, not as a local politician out to protect the vested interests of the local landowners and not with the iron hand of a northern Californian determined to fight to keep every drop of water from going south. (South is anywhere below your particular area; it doesn't necessarily mean southern California.) When tempers flared or lines were drawn in the sand, Bob got very calm and painstakingly deliberate. He didn't force consensus, he just pointed out the obvious—that the stakes were too high to walk away from the table and let someone else solve our differences.

I suppose that being raised a cowboy in Shasta County gave Bob Bosworth a lot of patience and a lot of confidence that, when people bother to get together around a table to negotiate, something good will happen. In January 1989, on behalf of the Upper Sacramento River Advisory Council, Bob Bosworth signed the foreword to the Upper Sacramento River Fisheries and Riparian Habitat Management Plan:

> [T]his plan was prepared by an advisory council and an action team of people representing a wide range of federal, State, and local agencies and private interests concerned with protecting the health of the Upper Sacramento River system. . . . The plan was developed in a spirit of cooperation and consensus among the participating agencies and individuals. . . .

The accomplishments of this advisory council were nothing short of remarkable.

So, I was extremely pleased to see Bob Bosworth waiting to get on the bus for the boat tour. I figured that if anyone knew what the mood of the district's water conference was, Bob would know. Then I could prepare my comments accordingly. I always enjoy my chance meetings with Bob Bosworth because I always come away with a fresh and positive attitude about solving California's water dilemma.

On the bus ride to the boat I did get some information from Bob about the water conference, but he spent most of the ride talking about growing up on a ranch in Shasta County before there was a Shasta Dam, when the salmon used to run up Burney Creek so thick that the ranch hands would scoop up a salmon from the creek and cook it in the bunkhouse after a long day's work. Bob talks about the Sacramento River as if he is talking about a lost love. In a way he is, since the history of the river and its creeks is the history of the Bosworth family and all the ranching families that came to the upper Sacramento River basin as pioneers and frontiersmen.

While I have worked on legislation and projects to restore the Sacramento River and its tributaries, I will never know and I will never experience the river that existed in Bob's childhood. But I love to hear him talk about it. I love to imagine it.

The bus ride and Bob's stories were over too quickly as we pulled up to the ferry boat that was to take us on our tour. There were a little over 100 "Delta tourists" on board and I guessed I was the least experienced of the entire group. Nonetheless, I headed up to the cabin to learn of my assignment from the tour directors.

I entered the cabin and introduced myself to Dan Pellegrini, one of the directors of the Contra Costa Water District. He quickly told me that I would give a brief talk about salmon in the Delta as soon as we got going. As salmon don't spend a great deal of their life in the Delta, I figured I could fill up a few minutes of time talking about salmon in general. So I found an out-of-the way seat on top of the map drawers and waited my turn.

Now in this cabin there were three older gentlemen, who I assumed were friends of Dan. After staring at me for some time, obviously sizing me up, one of them, Vince Bruno, came over and introduced himself and asked me what I did for a living. Over the years, I have learned never to introduce myself as either a lawyer, which I am, or as a lobbyist, which I have been at times. Since a lawyer/lobbyist can claim to be anything to anybody, I generally consider my audience and adjust my introduction accordingly. I told Vince I "represented" fishermen, which I do.

Well, Vince gave me the biggest Italian smile I had ever seen and yanked me off my perch and introduced me to his friends. I met Mike Dimaggio, a cousin of Joe's, and John Sparacino, ex-mayor of Martinez. I soon learned that Vince, Mike and John were former Delta commercial fishermen. Naturally, the fact that I represented fishermen made me a member of the family.

For the next three and a half hours I learned what it was like growing up in an Italian fishing community along the Delta. I learned that Joe Dimaggio was not born in Martinez, but as a "good Collinsville boy." I learned about fishing next to the big factory boats "to keep the wind from blowin' you outta your boat." Vince told the audience below what it was like fishing "under the wires" along the Carquinez Straits. How you would let your nets drift just close enough to the bridge so that the tide would not take your net beyond the bridge or else you would get pinched by Fish and Game. (Fish and Game was a thorn in the fisherman's side back then, too.) Keeping your boat from being pulled out with the tide was no easy feat with "two ton a salmon in your net."

Most of all, I revelled in watching three men talk about their youth and their connection to the Delta and the river they still love, even though it is so different and so much less productive. I saw the tears form in Vince's eyes as he talked about going fishing with his father and how they worked the lines and the nets together as a team. Mike Dimaggio, who was the most silent of the three, talked for fifteen minutes nonstop when Dan asked him about his fishing days in the Bay and the Delta. Mike relived those days when the Delta islands and their waterways were for fishermen.

I said very little during the tour; I just passed the microphone around and basked in the stories and history that was being retold. When the trip was over and we arrived in Vallejo, I felt like I should have paid the district for the opportunity it gave me.

I have driven over the Carquinez Straits more times than I can remember, I have flown over the Delta many times with my friend Clyde, I have gazed at maps of the Delta during interminable water negotiating sessions or hearings, but I have never had the Delta come to life the way it did thanks to Vince, Mike and John.

I realized then how much the fisheries and especially the salmon are a part of the heritage of California. For the stories that I listened to from Bob Bosworth and from Vince, Mike and John are similar in many ways to stories that I have heard from the ocean salmon fishermen I have represented since 1984. The salmon trollers talk of the days when they used to "hit the button" and go fishing when the weather seemed just right or you just "felt" the fishing would be good. They weren't bound to a fishing season developed by deskbound biologists whose eyes are glazed over by staring at irrelevant facts and figures about fishery population trends and nonsensical and unreliable predictors.

If the fishing wasn't good one day—well, there was tomorrow or the next day. If a season wasn't as good as the last—well, there was always the next season. If the salmon weren't biting off Sisters Rock—well, I overheard "on the air" that Pete had a bite off Bodega, so I might drift down there for a few days. If the wind starts to blow, I can always hide behind Point Arena until she stops.

There are damn few ocean salmon trollers left in California (or the entire west coast for that matter!). There are no Italian fishermen fishing off Port Costa or under the wires at Carquinez. No ranch hands scoop up the salmon out of Burney Creek anymore. With each loss, California loses some more of its heritage.

It was clear to me after that morning on the Delta, and it is clear to me now, that the King salmon that live off our coast from Morro Bay to Crescent City are a link not only to our past rich heritage, but a link to our future. The loss of this rich heritage affects our coastal fishing communities, the Bay and Delta and the upriver communities that await the return of the Kings. Unquestionably, in our history we have squandered our natural resources in a pell-mell rush to develop new frontiers. Unfortunately, as our resources diminish, the freedoms we once took for granted are also lost.

Several decades ago, the Central Valley Project was authorized because it was the consensus at that time that this project would be good for the development of our nation. Governor Pat Brown pushed for the authorization of the State Water Project because it offered opportunities for the growth and development of our state. Unquestionably, Californians have benefitted greatly from the development of these two vast water projects. Our nation has profited from the investment. Yet the costs to our natural heritage are catching up to us today.

Today, water developers and their allies within California look back on the development of these projects as halcyon days. It was a period of tranquility for water engineers before the enactment of the Endangered Species Act, National Environmental Policy Act (NEPA) and the California Environmental Quality Act (CEQA). Consensus was driven by the engines of commerce that were born from our frontier past.

Today, endangered species crop up like freshly planted rye grass to thwart the best engineered solution money can buy. CEQA and NEPA demand alternatives to be considered and even the alternative of doing nothing at all. As we seek to allocate our last drops of water, the public institutions we created only two decades ago appear impotent, more an impediment to progress than facilitator.

Is consensus on water policy possible in the 1990s or in the 21st century? Bob Bosworth and the Upper Sacramento River Advisory Council have proved that it is possible.

However, building consensus in the 1990s will be more complicated. This is true not because of the Endangered Species Act or NEPA and CEQA. It will be more difficult because there are very few frontiers to tap, if any. We also know more about the costs associated with our thirst. The full price for developed water halts even the most ardent water developer.

Bob Bosworth understands those costs when he remembers the Sacramento River of his youth. Vince Bruno knows what has been lost when he reminisces about fishing with his dad under the wires at Carquinez. "Sunny" Maahs, Fort Bragg salmon troller, understands what has been lost as he fishes when the wind is blowing, because there is no tomorrow in today's salmon fishery.

The ocean troll fishermen I represent know full well the cost of freedom. Faced with coast-wide closures to prevent the hypothetical take of *two* endangered winter run salmon, or month-long closures to allow spawners to return to rivers and streams that no longer have habitat in which to spawn, many have left the sea for it no longer offers the freedom they once enjoyed.

While my fishermen point a resentful finger at the benefactors of irrigation districts and state and federal facilities that destroy hundreds of thousands of juvenile and spawning salmon annually, the loss of freedom they have experienced at sea will soon be felt inland as we allocate our limited water supplies over an ever-increasing list of demands.

The last five years of drought foretell a bleak future for California unless we seize the opportunity to change our attitudes about the use of water. As it was when we built the water projects, parochialism over water policy and water rights must be adjusted for what is in the best interests of the state as a whole.

As Bob Bosworth counselled, we must be willing to "stay at the table" and resolve our differences, otherwise "someone" will solve them for us. When interest groups of every persuasion come together, there is common agreement that the status quo is unacceptable. The continued degradation of water quality and fisheries is unacceptable to fishermen. The unreliability of our "plumbing system" is unacceptable to those who must rely upon it for the future. The further degradation of our wetlands and riparian areas and our bays and estuaries are an unacceptable choice for our future. Unless we are willing to work toward solutions and make the public policy changes that are necessary for our future, our public institutions will allocate our water supply and with it our freedom in much the same way as our fishery management agencies allocate salmon for a fishery season.

As salmon trollers today can no longer "hit the button" and go fishing when they feel the fish are biting, future Californians may some day remember when they used to just "turn on the tap."

Like Bob Bosworth, I think we can do better.

New housing developments are a common sight in many parts of California, particularly the southern part of the state. The water supply for these homes and families is a serious concern. Photo credit: Metropolitan Water District of Southern California.

Urban

Unlike agricultural water users, whose water needs have peaked, the proportion of the water supply needed by urban users will continue to grow as the population increases and business and industry expand. If providing water to California up to the 1990s has been a challenge, the prospect of supplying water in the 21st century has many urban water suppliers frantically searching for ways to augment existing supplies.

California's population is expected to grow by 700,000 people a year. Urban water suppliers regard it as their responsibility to provide water to all who need it, not to use water to regulate growth. Not only must they provide water, but they must ensure a safe, high quality, reliable supply. While a variety of methods are being used to stretch existing supplies—water recycling, conservation, low water use appliances, xeriscaping, desalination, water marketing—many do not believe that these methods can provide enough water to the growing population. Some urban interests concede that agriculture is using water as efficiently as possible and that the environment must receive its share of water, and so look to additional facilities as the ultimate answer to California's water problems.

Bay Area interests stress, however, that any consensus effort must give first priority to protecting and improving the condition of the Bay-Delta Estuary. The estuary is valuable as an ecological resource and the conduit for water to most of the state. In protecting the Bay-Delta, we are protecting the future water supply.

AN HISTORIC ARGUMENT FOR COMPROMISE AND CONSENSUS

Carl Boronkay

Any discussion involving the seemingly polarized principles of water development and consensus building must acknowledge that consensus defined as "unanimity" is impossible to achieve. There are too many differences, too many positions, too many oxen waiting to be gored.

For more than 100 years, the din of polarized forces has stood in the way of the reasoned development of water resources. Even though such development has occurred from time to time, that tumult continues today. Some modicum of consensus has been, and will be, reached in the Legislature over the issue of transferring water from willing sellers to willing buyers. But such consensus, as has been the pattern in the past, is a reaction to pressure rather than the purity of doing the right thing at the right time to at least some benefit for all concerned.

The steps to what might be best called an acceptable consensus have included the identification of legitimate interests, reaching a compromise among those interests and moving ahead with the project with the full knowledge that some will object. What has worked in the past can work in the future, even while the number and diversity of interests has grown considerably.

Carl Boronkay has been general manager of Metropolitan Water District of Southern California since 1984. From 1980 to 1984, he served as general counsel at MWD. Before joining MWD, he worked in the California attorney general's office.

This is a simple concept of doing the greatest good for the greatest number, a concept not foreign to the relative affluence of the United States and well within the grasp of today's leaders in business, agriculture, water and the environment.

Development and environmentalism do not need to be mutually exclusive. A business person could be an environmentalist just as easily as one keenly interested in the environment can be a water agency manager. Those who choose to believe that such identifiers are exclusive are those on the fringes of each sector who tend to block consensus building by adopting an "all or nothing" position. Compromise, by definition, works.

Similarly, tossing about the term "vested interest" as some loathsome characteristic that cements one sector or another into a privately motivated and usually wrong-headed position presents a like obstacle to achieving a meaningful compromise. Those who get involved in issues, by definition, have a vested interest. Is such an interest in meeting the water demands of humans somehow less righteous than maintaining stream flow for a school of fish? Perhaps both objectives can be met through consensus and common sense.

A template for meeting today's water demands is available by looking backward 40 years or so to the creation of California's Department of Water Resources (DWR) and, before that, to the California Water Plan. Attempts at consensus were made much earlier, of course, but these two projects have statewide impacts, they are large-scale, and they remain important components of the state's water delivery system. The complete history of water development in California, however, from the first diversion ditch, or *zanja*, directing stream flow onto a mission field, to the State Water Resources Control Board's "Bay-Delta Hearings" of the late 1980s and early 1990s tends to be repetitive and offers little new in seeking resolutions to the myriad of problems that remain.

It was the California Water Plan that finally inventoried the state's water resources and sought to allocate them in a reasonable fashion. Reason being in the eye of the beholder, even this plan took nearly a decade to take shape and gain sufficient acceptance in the highly charged atmosphere of California politics in the 1950s.

Writing in the *Southern California Quarterly*, the journal of the Historical Society of Southern California, historian Harvey Grody tried to put things in perspective in 1978:

> From the immediate post-WWII years through the 1955 legislative session, California's legislative enactments reflecting statewide comprehensive perspectives on water resources development were sporadic in their appearance. There were several legislative acts during this period, e.g., (1) creation of the State Water Resources Board, (2) provision of fiscal support for the Board's statewide water investigations, (3) codification of water laws in the Water Code, (4) enlargement of the SWRB functions, (5) creation of the Water Pollution Control Board, and (6) authorization (without appropriations) of the Feather River Project as an integral unit of the Central Valley Project and the California Water Plan. There was also, however, (1) no particular interest shown in the California Water Plan as it was in its developmental stages, (2) considerable time spent on bickering over diversionary matters, e.g., attacking the national government and extended debate over abortive plans to purchase the Central Valley Project, (3) a narrow preoccupation with flood control matters, and (4) only failure in the most significant area of statewide importance, i.e., reorganization of the myriad of water agencies into a unified Department of Water Resources.

The Legislature had failed to create DWR in 1953 and again in 1955. The Feather River Project and San Luis appropriations were made the following year, coincident with the formation of DWR, only to return to impasse in 1957-1958.

Compromise solutions were sought to move along with the Feather River Project and the joint construction (with the federal government) of San Luis Reservoir, but politics continued to invade the process. Of little help was a rift between Gov. Goodwin Knight and State Engineer A.D. Edmonston over the role and leadership of DWR. State Attorney General Edmund G. "Pat" Brown assured the governor that his office was properly the chief legal counsel for the new department—one of the questions that pitted Knight against Edmonston. But, Brown argued, resolution of this question was not significant enough to delay the formation of DWR.

Brown's willingness to give a little and allow each side to claim a modest victory was not only significant, but indicative of the political skill that would be necessary to continue plans for assuring all California an adequate water supply. Indeed, it was Brown as governor who signed into law the Burns-Porter Act in 1959, achieved an appropriation for water resources development and gained acceptance for the California Water Plan. The governor's skills were political, to be sure, but more important, he was able to identify those interests that really mattered before wasting his influence on those which did not.

Consensus of water interests is evident in a capsulated history of the State Water Project (SWP) in *Aqueduct Magazine*, a publication of Metropolitan Water District:

> The State Water Plan (predecessor of the California Water Plan), developed under the leadership of State Engineer Edward Hyatt in 1931, led to the basic design of the federal Central Valley Project to deliver surplus northern water to the Central Valley.
>
> In the middle of the depression, however, bonds for this project proved to be unsalable and the CVP was turned over to the federal government.
>
> A detailed inventory of the state's water resources was completed in 1947 and, as a result of this plan and other studies projecting future supply and demand, the California Water Plan was created in 1957 and adopted by the Legislature two years later.
>
> The Feather River and Sacramento-San Joaquin Delta Diversion projects (Feather River Act) had been approved by the state Legislature in 1951. But, like the Central Valley Project before it, financing was unavailable.
>
> The Feather River Act (forerunner of the SWP) is significant, however, because it provided the basic authorization for the project. The Burns-Porter Act, officially called the "California Water Resources Development Bond Act," provided the financing for the project in 1959. The California Water Plan, approved by the Legislature in the same year, includes the physical facilities in the Burns-Porter Act as well as other water development philosophies.
>
> The act authorized $1.75 billion in general obligation bonds to complete work on the water project which began in 1957 when highways and railroads at the site of Oroville Dam and Reservoir were relocated following disastrous floods.

Ultimately, the State Water Project is committed to deliver 4,230,000 acre-feet of water to 30 contractors statewide. Metropolitan Water District is, by far, the largest of those contractors with a maximum entitlement of 2,011,500 acre-feet of water.

Major projects on the SWP include Oroville, Castaic, Pyramid, Perris and Silverwood reservoirs, the Governor Edmund G. Brown California Aqueduct, eight power stations and 22 pumping plants, including the A.D. Edmonston unit which boosts water nearly 2,000 feet over the Tehachapis—the largest single lift in the world.

Gov. Brown's unique style of consensus building led to the greatest water storage and delivery system ever. This system has helped California grow to its dominant position in the world as a producer of food and fiber, a vacation destination, a polyglot society second to none and a highly attractive place to live. Yet, the SWP today is essentially inadequate in all but the wettest of years.

The consensus that enabled the SWP to begin failed in the early 1970s when a planned storage facility on the Eel River at Dos Rio was rejected. Interestingly, the viewpoint of the then-emerging environmentalist movement was "don't build a dam at all," while those responsible for meeting future water needs felt it shouldn't be built *yet.* Time intervened and the delay ultimately buried this project. Later, with the SWP well under way, the question shifted to the construction of a facility that would carry Sacramento River water across the Sacramento-San Joaquin Delta without commingling with the waters of the Delta itself. The Burns-Porter Act clearly calls for such a facility, but the language is vague enough to allow debate and, thus, seek consensus.

After nearly a decade, such consensus in the Legislature was won and the Peripheral Canal was expressly authorized. Today, the words "Peripheral Canal" are rarely uttered without modifiers such as "ill-fated" or "rejected." Some even facetiously refer to the "P" word.

In this case, consensus was achieved by the people's representatives, the Legislature, only to have that agreement overturned by the people themselves. The question raised is, "Is there a meaningful consensus group other than the electorate?"

The answer seems to be, "The more divisive the issue, the more broad the consensus group needs to be." Yet, it is the need to appeal to so many—the Christmas tree approach to consensus building—that can shatter an agreement.

Without any particular argument that the Peripheral Canal was or was not the right thing to do, the fact is that the enabling legislation, Senate Bill 200, was viewed by some as too oriented toward fish protection and by others as too harmful to the Delta fishery. Some argued that it offered the best protection for the environment while others claimed it would lead to the destruction of the area.

SB 200's forerunner, SB 346, never made it through the Legislature. It started lean and ended its life as a freight train pulling lots of extra cars unrelated to the primary objective. What began as consensus-seeking developed into a series of trade-offs that made SB 346 objectionable to nearly everyone. It was, one might suggest, compromised to death. Later, SB 200 supporters went in the opposite direction with a trimmed down "take it or leave it" package. The package was left.

Soon after the election, interest groups cropped up with what they perceived as a more reasonable approach to water development. Those in the south saw the defeat as a threat to a stable water supply from the SWP. Those in the north saw the election as a sort of turning point and gathered under a "no more water south" banner. Some used "consensus" as part of their name: the Committee for Water Policy Consensus, for example. There was no pretense, however, that statewide water development consensus was on the immediate agenda of this group. Rather, this Bay Area organization insisted on alternatives to the export of water to state project contractors. As a counterpart, a southern group, the Southern California Water Committee, formed in order to achieve a consensus, at least in the south, to increase the amount of water delivered through the project.

Two consensus groups operating at different ends of a continuum are unlikely to achieve the desired agreement. Yet compromise remains possible and, indeed, has culminated in such matters as urban conservation and water reclamation. The clock, measuring not time, but supply and demand, is ticking, however. Popular wisdom is that long-term efficiencies do not control during an emergency. The overriding criterion, whether responding to an earthquake or reacting to famine, is to solve the problem at hand. All other considerations, be they environmental, financial or otherwise, move to second place.

That should not happen to California when water development is the topic. The reality is that additional water development is going to happen and there is still time for that to happen in an orderly, sensible fashion . . . but not much time. California's population is increasing on the order of 700,000 people a year. Its dependable water resources have diminished substantially. The drought that continued through 1991 is viewed by most consumers as transitory, yet even when the present drought caused by lack of precipitation ends, droughts caused by the lack of resources development will recur with increasing frequency and intensity.

There is no populated region of the state that will escape from the hardships caused by looming water shortages. Perhaps this realization should serve as the focus of statewide consensus. It is, after all, agreement across California that will lead to solutions. Regional consensus building can effectively assist in the distribution of water supplies available to that region, but are largely ineffective in increasing those supplies that originate in another hydrologic basin unless such regionalism becomes a part of a movement to increase the availability of potable water supplies throughout the state.

Consensus requires the identification of responsible parties: water managers, politicians, consumers, environmentalists, farmers. Many people will reside in two or more of these interest groups and the "us versus them" mentality must vanish. Today, no particular interest group's water problem can be solved without, at the same time, addressing the problems of the other interest groups.

A second step is to develop plans that comprehensively balance all reasonable probabilities, including consumer costs, growth patterns, ecological impacts and related issues. The cost of environmental mitigation has skyrocketed to a point where it has become a major component of the total cost of a project, if that project can ever be built. This is not an argument to do away with the process. It is an argument, however, for reasonableness in making decisions related to the welfare of people and the environment.

Third, the various legitimate interests must work out their differences with an eye to "reasonableness" and an understanding that the "do nothing" alternative is no longer tolerable when discussing a continuation of water development in California. Within the scope of reaching consensus, those intent on development at all cost and those committed solely to environmental protection will find some middle ground. Metropolitan, for example, is deeply involved in water reclamation and conservation as important but partial alternatives to construction. Those at the extreme end of the environmental movement must, in turn, realize that virtually no human activity is free from environmental impacts. For that matter, no living organism exists whose actions do not impact another organism. What is required is balance over extremism, reason over rhetoric. Somewhere between the bending of a blade of meadow grass and massive environmental damage, a reasonable solution can be found.

Fourth, we have developed, and urge others to develop, the concept of "Best Management Practices (BMPs)." In terms of water use, BMPs represent conservation measures or processes that have been developed through a consensus process with water agencies and the environmental community. In essence, BMPs are those conservation efforts that can be reasonably accomplished. After implementation, it is understood that any additional water supply beyond that accounted for as a reduction in demand requires additional water projects.

Finally, the various interest groups must resolve that once agreement is reached it is time to move along to other issues. Much of California's watershed has been studied to the point of exhaustion. Minutia has crippled some programs and fatally delayed others while the impact of not doing the project at all goes unstudied. This myopia can lead to the inefficiencies of emergency reactions when even perfunctory research is not possible within the time constraints of solving a particular serious problem instantly.

A case in point is Los Banos Grandes, an off-stream reservoir of the SWP. Enabling legislation was authored by an assemblyman who is one of the SWP's severest critics. Yet, there is recognition that additional water storage south of the Delta is of great benefit to those in the north as well as the south. Consensus has been reached on the need, the location, general size and other issues that once divided those benefitting from the project and those seeking to freeze the SWP at its current, inadequate level of ability to deliver water. After all that, interest groups are now raising environmental questions as though there is an alternative site—which there is not—or an alternative to additional water storage—which there is not. Building Los Banos is not anti-environmental; it is pro-people in the most reasonable fashion practical. Still, its inability to please "all the people all the time" may stymie it with no substitute in sight.

In sum, if the 1950s and 1960s are remembered as the decades when California took giant steps toward solving huge water problems, the 1980s will be remembered as the decade when studies outweighed solutions and the state's population caught up with, or even surpassed, the ability of the state to provide water. Since water development, by its very nature, takes a long time, it is possible that we are in an emergency situation today without fully realizing it and without adequately responding to it. As a society, we do not elect the "do nothing" course as a matter of overt consensus, but rather as a lack thereof. In that vacuum, the will of a few "activists" can effectively block the needs of many by "exposing" the cost of a project or decrying perceived environmental damage without concern over the serious impacts of failing to build it. Theirs is the easier argument since they demand proof of things that cannot be proven or indict on narrow issues of the moment without regard to the future.

Interest groups need to become less strident and all Californians need to assist government in the formulation and implementation of creative, efficient solutions to existing problems. Consensus is not defined as "all," but rather "a majority of opinion" that is harmonious and agreeable. Californians have achieved consensus in the past. We must achieve consensus for the future.

Since urban water users are bound to feel the brunt of sustained shortages, and serious damage to the overall economy will result from deficiencies in municipal supply, urban agency managers have taken the initiative in creating a dialogue with representatives of both environmentalist organizations and agricultural districts. With this has come improved understanding of the whole water picture and greater trust among the participants—essential elements in achieving consensus.

In the past, consensus was generally attempted through trade-offs among interests who collectively had enough muscle to interrupt the process at will. While this approach undoubtedly continues to play a part, a broader view is emerging—water problems should no longer be considered the exclusive concern of a particular interest group. Rather, each is being asked to assume the role of the others in formulating its proposed solutions to water problems. This change of mind-set should result in the ultimate consensus where, indeed, the greatest good occurs for the greatest numbers.

CALIFORNIA WATER SHORTAGE POSES CHALLENGES FOR STATE POLICYMAKERS

Kirk West

There is an old theory about water supplies in California: "There is enough water for all foreseeable future needs—it is just a mater of developing it and getting it from areas of surplus to water-deficient areas."

The reality at the start of the 1990s is that no water projects are being built, no significant new water for cities has been added to the supply system in two decades, existing water supplies will suffer a net reduction in the next few years, and plans on the drawing board for new projects face difficult political and legal hurdles.

Overall, the days of water surpluses in California are over. The redundancy of supply is gone. Water shortages, always the critical concern of California life, will dominate our future as shortages become a way of life.

Life with water shortages is being called the new "California water ethic." It could include a number of different experiences, some cosmetic, some painful. The ethic contemplates that the projected 40 million people in the state in the year 2010 will use the same amount of water as the 30 million people in the state at the end of 1990.

Kirk West is president of the California Chamber of Commerce.

Instead of planning water development projects to meet demand, the water ethic calls for xeriscaping (drought-tolerant landscaping), 1.6 gallon-per-flush toilets and charging large-volume water users., i.e. business, a price that escalates as the amount used increases.

Even though California has sufficient water that can be developed in an environmentally responsible way, some commentators are promoting the idea of supplying the population increase with water from farms. Arizona took this route in the 1980s. With no water to develop, Arizona opted to limit agriculture so there would be sufficient water for cities and manufacturing. Arizona chose to depend on other regions of the United States and on Mexico to supply agricultural products.

If California were to follow Arizona's lead, the decision would have massive repercussions on the California economy.

CURRENT WATER USAGE

Per capita water use in the San Francisco Bay area and Los Angeles is about 190 gallons a day. This includes household uses, business and government services. For residential use only, the figure is about 120 gallons a day per person for showers, cooking and landscaping. An additional 4,533 gallons of water a day are needed to provide each person with food.

About half of the water in the state has been developed, with agriculture using about 80 percent and cities using about 20 percent. But compared to the total amount of water in the river systems in the state, agriculture consumes only 31 percent and 29 percent has been legally dedicated to the environment through wild and scenic river designations and water released into San Francisco Bay and the Sacramento-San Joaquin Delta.

Although less than half of the potential water has been developed, only about 5 million acre-feet of water is considered to be economically developable. The amount of developable water lost by designation of north coast rivers as wild and scenic is 17.8 million acre-feet, which could yield enough water to serve population growth well into the 22nd century.

California uses more ground water each year than is naturally replaced. This overdraft amounts to about 2 million acre-feet a year and much of it occurs in the San Joaquin Valley. A stable surface water supply must be found to stop the overdraft, or the costs of pumping and the depletion of aquifers eventually will force hundreds of thousands of acres of agriculture out of production.

URBAN WATER DEMAND

Except for the agricultural overdraft problem, development of new supplies to serve urban areas will be the primary concern of state water planners. Urban areas with the largest increase in demand for water will be Santa Ana, San Diego, Los Angeles, Sacramento, the San Francisco Bay area and the San Joaquin Valley.

Urban water supplies are now about in balance with demand, but population growth is adding a city the size of San Francisco—about 700,000 people—every year. The urban water supply problem is compounded by expected reductions in existing supplies due to a complex combination of federal and state regulatory requirements, court decisions, water rights and environmental concerns.

If no new water is developed to meet these demands, shortages and rationing will occur on a regular basis. The Department of Water Resources (DWR) now estimates that there will not be enough water in 50 percent of the years for cities served by the State Water Project, which is the major statewide water system for urban areas.

The department also estimates a new water need of 18,000 acre-feet per year for each 100,000 new residents in an urban area. This figure represents all urban needs for those people, including domestic uses, jobs and government services and includes a large water conservation assumption.

Assuming population growth tapers off during the next 20 years (the lead time for adding significant new water supplies), the additional water demand in the year 2010 for 10 million new residents in the state will be 1.8 million acre-feet if conservation efforts are successful. In 1983, DWR assumed urban areas would save 955,000 acre-feet of water a year by 2010 with vigorous conservation efforts. If this amount of conservation is not achieved, the amount of urban demand will increase correspondingly.

SUPPLY REDUCTIONS

The State Water Project supplies water to 30 of the several hundred water agencies in the state, including cities in the San Francisco Bay area and central and southern California. It can reliably deliver only 2.3 million acre-feet per year compared to annual water contracts totaling 4.2 million acre-feet. If no new facilities are developed, the amount of deliveries will actually decline in the future as more water is used in the Sacramento Valley, which has higher priority water rights than the project contractors. None of the potential ways to increase supply for the project have been approved by state and federal environmental officials.

Court and regulatory actions could also reduce total water supplies in the state in the next 20 years. New water development projects will be needed to meet both increased demand and to replace lost sources of current supplies. These losses include:

* Water from the Colorado River Aqueduct will be reduced due to a 1964 U.S. Supreme Court decision that divided water in the lower Colorado River. Arizona is the net beneficiary of the water lost by southern California.

* The city of Los Angeles has lost several legal skirmishes involving about 17 percent of its water supply, mostly from the Mono Lake basin.

* Ground water contamination has forced many local water agencies to turn off pumps.

* Water quality regulations are making previously usable drinking water unusable.

* New Delta water quality standards, which will be set by the State Water Resources Control Board, also could affect supplies.

In the proceedings before the State Board, requests have been made to improve fisheries by reducing water exports by up to 1.5 million acre-feet per year.

* The listing of the winter-run salmon as a threatened species in the Sacramento River by the federal government may have an as yet unquantified effect on water supplies.

* Legal challenges to existing water rights are likely to occur under the public trust doctrine. As a result, water supplies for cities and farms could be reallocated to recreation and fisheries.

* The federal Central Valley Project, which serves both cities and farms, is not immune to losing water supplies to a variety of environmental claims as 40-year water contracts are renewed.

CUT WATER FOR AGRICULTURE?

Many commentators use the figures showing that farms take 80 percent of the water and cities receive only 20 percent to claim agriculture should not waste water and that the water agriculture can save will be used to build the cities of California's future. The "80/20" argument is a variation of the Arizona type solution, or "phase agriculture out."

This theory of water supply has been met with skepticism. Detailed irrigation water use studies show there is very little potential water savings in the Central Valley. The pumping costs for water are so high, whether from ground water or delivery by water projects uphill from the Sacramento-San Joaquin Delta, that water conservation produces profits and prevents bankruptcy on farms. Also, water is constantly reused in the Central Valley stream systems, so any surplus water that might drain off a field is pumped out of the river downstream by another farmer or a city. By contrast, in urban coastal areas most of the water is used once and released into the ocean.

Most agricultural water in the San Joaquin Valley is subject to shortages during drought years and would not be useful for municipal and industrial requirements to meet dry-year demand. Unless the amount of irrigated acreage is forcibly reduced, farm water savings will be small. But assuming there can be savings, there will be a strong interest in the value in retaining that water for additional agriculture or urbanization. Almost 5 million people live in the Central Valley and the economic activity in the valley is directly linked to surrounding agricultural operations.

In some areas, there are opportunities to conserve agricultural water. On the Colorado River, 100,000 acre-feet a year of irrigation water is being conserved and transferred to cities, and it may be possible to conserve an additional 150,000 to 200,000 acre-feet per year.

To the extent state policies might reduce agricultural water use, California will become more dependent on food supplies from the midwest, which depends on unpredictable summer rains to grow crops.

FEWER OPTIONS

The 1957 California Water Plan listed a series of options to supply water as demand increased. A number of the sources of supply identified in the 1957 plan have been eliminated.

Court decisions and legislation have reduced the amount of water available to satisfy future demand. A major potential water development was lost when major north coast rivers were designated as wild and scenic by the state in 1973 and the federal government in 1982.

Several other water development projects have been stopped or foreclosed by legislation, generally due to concern over preserving a species or scenic area. These lost opportunities, which considerably restrict future supply options, include:

　* Pamo Dam in San Diego County;

　* Rodgers Crossing Dam on the Kings River near Fresno;

　* Clavey-Wards Ferry Reservoir on the Tuolumne River near Modesto;

　* Auburn Dam on the American River near Sacramento (stopped in 1975 due to earthquake concerns).

As each potential water development source is eliminated and local communities are unable to supply their own water needs, increased attention is focused on the Sacramento-San Joaquin

Delta and the state and federal water projects as the supply of last resort.

THE DELTA

As the focal point of political debates on water development in recent years, the current Delta water transfer situation is a technical and environmental problem needing a solution. Because most of the surplus water is north of the Delta and the water deficient areas are to the south and west, Delta transfer issues are the key to other future water supply options as well.

The water export pumps regularly reverse the flow of one of California's major rivers, the San Joaquin. It is understandable that there is ongoing damage to the fisheries in the Delta.

The Delta stands between the Sacramento River, which carries water released from storage reservoirs to the north of the Delta and the export pumps (to the south of the Delta). Because there is no direct connection between the two points, water is moved out the Sacramento River and up the San Joaquin River, and about one-third of the water becomes contaminated with salt in the mixing zone between the salt water and fresh water in the western part of the Delta.

Recently, the salt particles (bromides) that mix with the water flowing upstream to the pumps were identified as the most persistent trihalomethanes (THMs) precursors, a potential carcinogen that forms when organic and salt chemicals react with the chlorine used to disinfect drinking water. They also are the most costly to remove before the water is delivered as drinking water to two-thirds of the state's population.

DELTA OPTIONS

New surface or ground water storage facilities north or south of the Delta will depend on a better method to transfer water from the Sacramento River to the export pumps.

The Delta options include reducing water exports, maintaining the status quo or building a better transfer facility.

The Department of Water Resources released draft environmental impact reports in 1990 that describe facilities to more efficiently transfer water through the Delta by using existing channels in the eastern Delta.

Use of those channels would bypass the salt water problem, save some of the water now wasted and solve some of the fishery problems. The reverse flows on the San Joaquin River, a problem mostly for the striped bass, could be reduced; however, salmon entering the interior Delta could be a problem.

Another approach would be to build an isolated channel, the Peripheral Canal, around the Delta. This approach may solve the salt water, water waste and fishery problems all at once.

A newer proposal would avoid the Delta problems altogether by taking the water closer to the storage source and delivering it directly to the export pumps.

POSSIBLE SUPPLY ADDITIONS

Most methods of meeting future demands will rely on an efficient way to transfer water through or around the Delta. Most of the proposals are likely to encounter permitting obstacles and objections from environmental groups that oppose any new water development and place priority on instream flows.

Enlarging Shasta Dam

The most promising potential water supply source would be to triple the largest reservoir in the state—Shasta Dam on the Sacramento River. The reservoir storage would be increased from 4.5 million acre-feet to 14 million acre-feet and provide enough water to serve about 8 million people.

Purchase and sale of Central Valley Project water

On a temporary basis, some water developed by the federal Central Valley Project may be available for sale to cities outside the Central Valley.

Many agricultural and environmental interests fear "another Owens Valley." The Los Angeles Aqueduct carries water from the Owens Valley to the Los Angeles urban area. The controversy surrounding these water purchases still goes on today. Photo credit: Los Angeles Department of Water and Power.

Los Banos Grandes Reservoir

Off-stream storage south of the Delta, such as the proposed 1.7 million acre-feet Los Banos Grades Reservoir near Los Banos, will depend on federal permits to increase pumping from the Delta.

Cottonwood Creek

Although needed to help control flood flows in the Sacramento River, this potential project to the west of Red Bluff and Redding is not being actively pursued.

Ground water storage

The proposed Kern Water Bank could yield 140,000 acre-feet a year. This project may depend on whether state and federal agencies will allow additional exports from the Delta until the reverse flow problem is resolved.

Water transfers

Trading in water represents an opportunity and a liability. The entity holding water rights and offering the water for sale may be subjected to public trust claims requesting a modification of the water rights to increase flows for fisheries and recreation. Although there may be profit in selling the water for one or more years, the water rights holder could suffer a long-term loss of water. Transfers within basins are common, but where they involve increased Delta exports, they suffer the same problems as other exports.

The permanent transfer of irrigation water to urban areas will continue to be controversial within the agricultural community if the transfer would affect the economic future of the region. And temporary transfers cannot be the basis for meeting the needs of new cities.

Two other options don't depend on the Delta, but other problems must be overcome for these alternatives to yield more water.

Wastewater reclamation

Although the use of this source of water is expected to double by 2010, health considerations have limited the uses of reclaimed water to irrigation and an increasing demand in manufacturing. If separate piping systems were allowed for commercial activities, such as separating the drinking water from water for flushing toilets in buildings, considerably more wastewater could be used.

Desalination

Desalination of sea water or wastewater is costly and consumes a great deal of energy. New nuclear reactor technology may make desalination economical in the future by providing the energy and the heat to process the salt water into drinking water, but there will be objections to such projects.

SOLUTIONS NEEDED

A solution to the Delta transfer question remains the key to resolving the state's looming water supply problem. Conservation is a crucial part of the water supply formula, but it already is factored into the demand equation. What the state chooses to do—or not do—about its water supply will have significant long-term impact on the California economy. Competition or the threat of competition over existing water supplies has created uncertainty as to the source, the amount available and the cost of future supplies for many users. Investment decisions by California businesses will be affected by whether there is a reliable supply of water for agriculture and cities. Given the 20-year lead time on water development projects, California has long passed the deadline for finding a way to meet the water needs of the 21st century.

The famous San Francisco skyline, with a view from the San Francisco Bay of the growing urban need for more water. How to protect natural resources such as the Bay and supply water is a critical issue in consensus negotiations. Photo credit: Water Education Foundation.

ACHIEVING CONSENSUS ON WATER POLICY

Sunne Wright McPeak

SUMMARY

It is not only possible, but essential, that we achieve consensus on water policy in California. The state's economic vitality and environmental quality are at risk. Fortunately, the ability to achieve consensus is definitely within the grasp of state leaders, if they are sincere about addressing the key issues and if they utilize a consensus process to reach agreement. In fact, meeting the state's future water needs for at least the next 20 years is a relatively simple problem technically to solve, in comparison to all the other hurdles facing California. Leadership from all sectors of the state, dedicated to a "new water ethic" and with a clear vision of the opportunities for consensus, is needed to make this happen.

Since the defeat of two statewide water measures by the voters in 1982—the Peripheral Canal referendum (Proposition 9) and a water management initiative (Proposition 13)—it has been evident that the only way to achieve progress on water issues is by building broad-based consensus instead of forcing legislation through a political process. Those elections reflected a new reality

Contra Costa County Supervisor Sunne Wright McPeak is a founding member and chair of the San Francisco Bay-Delta-based Committee for Water Policy Consensus. McPeak co-chairs the State Water Conservation Coalition.

in water politics, whereby it is possible for any one region of the state or coalition of interest groups to block actions of all the rest. We can literally checkmate each other on the water chessboard. The result is political gridlock and policy stalemate. However, every time a sincere effort has been made by key parties to reach consensus, progress has been made.

A consensus approach has produced significant accomplishments in water policy during the last decade. Those achievements include: authorization of Los Banos Grandes reservoir for additional water storage; approval of the Coordinated Operation Agreement (COA) and enactment of HR 3113 to coordinate operations of the State Water Project (SWP) and the federal Central Valley Project (CVP); completion of the "two agency fish agreement" between the Department of Water Resources (DWR) and the Department of Fish and Game (DFG) to mitigate fish losses at the export pumps; agreement for exchange of water between the Metropolitan Water District of Southern California and the Imperial Irrigation District; passage of legislation to reconstruct and maintain Delta levees; agreement for protection of the managed portion of Suisun Marsh; development of a conservation agreement among urban water districts, environmental groups and other public-interest organizations to implement "Best Management Practices" (BMPs) that will generate approximately 1 million acre-feet annually of additional water supply by the end of the decade; agreement regarding identification of the potential for 244,000 acre-feet additional fresh water displaced by the year 2000 through water recycling, reuse and reclamation; completion of a citizens' advisory committee report and recommendations on San Joaquin Valley drainage; and passage of the Water Conservation in Landscaping Act and agreement on a model water efficient landscape ordinance for all cities and counties in California.

Some of the toughest policy questions remain: environmental protections for the Bay-Delta Estuary; improved Delta transfer facilities; and providing an adequate, reliable, quality water supply for future demands. The next phase of statewide consensus negotiations must deal with all these issues in order to avoid a shortfall in California's water supply by the year 2000. Agreement will be achieved on meeting California's future water needs only when state leaders understand that a policy package comprising these issues is the key to achieving consensus.

This approach will not only resolve the most immediate, difficult issues but will also produce benefits for all regions of the state. It is important to note that the consensus package does not include consideration of a Peripheral Canal or any other isolated Delta transfer facility at this time. Resurrection of the Peripheral Canal concept at this point in negotiations will result in confrontation and will delay consensus. The non-isolated water banking proposal is a superior policy and engineering approach for achieving consensus in this decade.

Finally, it must be underscored that statewide consensus will be achieved sooner with strong leadership from the governor, his administration and the Legislature. They are wise to encourage and support the current consensus efforts that have been initiated outside of the formal state government structure. It is essential that the key interest groups and stakeholders come to agreement among themselves before state policy can be successfully adopted and implemented. But strong, aggressive leadership from the governor in partnership with the Legislature to facilitate the consensus process would produce significant water policy agreement in the immediate future. And that would be a great benefit to California's economy and environment.

OPPORTUNITIES FOR POLICY CONSENSUS

The context for consensus is created by the adoption of a "new water ethic" which establishes a dramatic departure from previous water practices and past water politics. Put simply, a new water ethic realizes that water is a limited natural resource that cannot be wasted and recognizes the need to preserve and to protect the environment for future generations. A new water ethic reflects a fundamental shift in thinking which rejects huge water development projects as the only way to meet future water needs and which advocates maximizing the efficient use of the current supply as an essential part of the equation. It sets forth the prerequisite that environmental safeguards be enacted before more water is diverted or developed for consumptive uses, and it delineates the principle that new water development projects be approved only if they are environmentally safe and economically sound.

Historically, controversies have erupted over water when it was perceived that one region would benefit at the expense of another or when the environment was being sacrificed for the profit of the economy. A new water ethic defines the common ground upon which negotiations can take place to reach consensus about meeting future water needs. It brings together all the stakeholders and interested parties in a new relationship built upon a different premise that avoids the basic conflicts of the past.

Embracing a new water ethic (or its policy equivalent) is an essential first step towards consensus. Achieving consensus, however, depends also on the ability of state leaders to accurately identify the opportunities for agreement and the appropriate sequence for seizing them. An opportunity for consensus exists when stakeholders are willing to concede something desired by others in order to gain more in return than is assured by the status quo. An opportunity will become a reality only if all stakeholders win. Further, the sequence in which issues are addressed can often be very critical. It is usually wise to tackle the relatively easier or less controversial issues first in order to build trust and a track record of success.

Over the last decade the successful consensus efforts have worked through a series of important issues, demonstrating that agreement on water policy is possible with the right approach. Generally, those efforts have addressed how to make the current water system work more efficiently. The issues yet to be resolved are the toughest because they are either the most difficult technically (involving supply reallocations or new construction) or the most controversial (dealing with Delta transfer facilities). However, we can no longer avoid coming to terms with these issues. Failure to do so will result in continuing degradation of the Bay-Delta Estuary and the prospect of shortfalls in water supply by the end of the decade. Therefore, the next round of statewide consensus negotiations must address a certain set of remaining issues, including: ecological deterioration of the Bay-Delta Estuary; improved Delta transfer facilities to mitigate impacts of the current export system; and reliability of an adequate, quality water supply to meet future demands. Only when all of these problems are addressed simultaneously is there a potential for trade-offs in negotiations such that all parties can have a "win" and gain more than they have by doing nothing.

The framework for reaching consensus on water policy to resolve the above problems must contain at least the following three components: adequate environmental protections for the Bay-Delta Estuary; conservation and efficient use of the existing supply; and construction of water banking facilities to improve Delta transfer of exports and to reduce environmental damage. Each of these three components encompasses several elements and implementation steps, but it is the combination of these three components that creates the opportunity for consensus and the possibility that all parties win.

Why is the combination of the above three components in a policy package key to achieving consensus? The most important bottom-line issue for the Bay-Delta region is protection of the Bay-Delta Estuary, the foundation of the area's ecology and economy. The most pressing concern for southern California is meeting future water demands with a reliable water supply of acceptable quality. In the past, the struggle resulting from each region independently pursuing these two goals has been perceived as a "zero sum game." It was thought that if southern California expanded its water supply, it meant more exports out of the Delta and less water for the environment. Likewise, it was assumed that increased environmental protections for the Bay-Delta Estuary meant a reduced water supply for southern California and the San Joaquin Valley. But this is not necessarily the case. If additional water can be generated from conservation and more efficient use of the existing supply, then some future demand can be met without increased Delta exports. Also, water banking holds the prospect of actually expanding the "water pie" in the Delta so that both environmental protections can be enhanced and the water supply increased. However, new facilities must be constructed in order to implement water banking. But there will never be consensus on any new Delta facilities until adequate Bay-Delta environmental protections are guaranteed and unless the efficient use of the current developed water supply is assured. Hence, all three components (Bay-Delta protections, conservation and efficient use and water banking) must be addressed simultaneously and combined in a policy package in order to achieve consensus.

Note that this approach also avoids the tired debate of "conservation versus construction." The reality is we need to do both. We must implement all feasible conservation measures not only to fulfill the spirit of a new water ethic but also to enable us to meet future demands until new construction projects are completed. And we need new construction not only to meet additional future demands but also to mitigate the negative impacts of the current Delta export system.

The following describes in more detail the specific elements and implementation steps of the three components.

ENVIRONMENTAL PROTECTIONS FOR THE BAY-DELTA ESTUARY

There is no state law that pertains directly to environmental protection for the Bay-Delta Estuary. The Delta Protection Act addresses only the Delta. It is time that state law acknowledges the reality of nature, namely that the San Francisco Bay/Sacramento-San Joaquin Delta Estuary is a dynamic ecosystem that must be protected as a whole. Therefore, it is critical that the cornerstone of sufficient and complete environmental protections for the estuary be the enactment of a law (or provision in a policy package) that establishes "it is the policy of the state and all of its officers to protect and preserve all reasonable and beneficial uses of the Bay-Delta Estuary." The law should further require that DWR manage the SWP in a manner that mitigates the negative impacts of its operation. Although the exact wording of a Bay-Delta protection act is open for discussion, the essence of this concept must be embedded in state law. While scientific data over time may alter the specific standards or regulations imposed to comply with the law, this approach is critical because it establishes as a matter of law that the Bay-Delta Estuary shall not be destroyed and conveys that there is a point beyond which Delta exports cannot be increased, regardless of other competing interests. Advocates for the Bay-Delta region would also prefer to include this kind of environmental protection in the state constitution along with the area-of-origin and county-of-origin laws.

Further, in order to reach consensus on construction of facilities that would have the potential of exporting more water out of the Delta, it is essential that the State Water Resources Control Board (SWRCB) be required to set adequate and complete water quality standards for the Delta and Bay before the export levels are actually increased. The new standards must provide for increased spring flows, reduced pumping in critical months, appropriate temperature controls and improved salinity objectives. It is important to note that consensus on facilities does not depend on first setting the new standards but rather on requiring that new facilities cannot be operated for the purposes of increasing export levels until the new standards have been set by the SWRCB and are in force. Articulating this kind of "sequencing" for elements of a policy package helps facilitate consensus.

The biggest fear related to any new Delta facilities, isolated or non-isolated, is the prospect of taking more water out of the system at the wrong times. So it is essential that key environmental safeguards be adopted to guarantee that any facility will be operated properly.

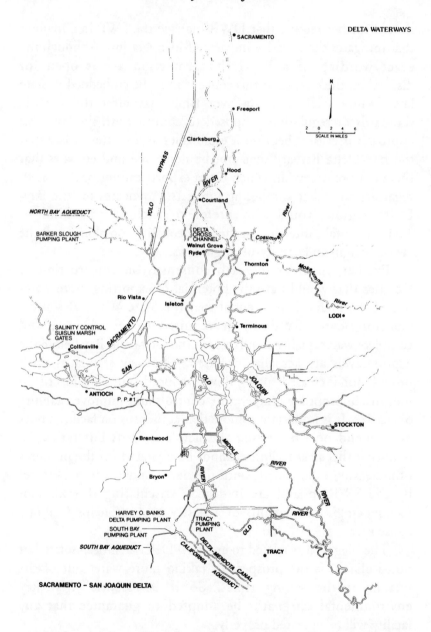

The Sacramento-San Joaquin Delta is a key element in the California water system and the consensus negotiations in process today. Most water interests will acknowledge that protecting and preserving the Delta is the first priority in solving California's water problems. Photo credit: California Department of Water Resources.

CONSERVATION AND EFFICIENT USE

There are several important elements in this component of a policy package. They include: implementation of urban conservation programs as encompassed in the BMP agreement; construction of water recycling and reuse projects to generate at least 244,000 acre-feet additional fresh water displaced by the year 2000; enactment of water marketing to encourage and facilitate voluntary transfers; implementation of efficient agricultural irrigation practices, including the establishment of goals or targets for system-wide conservation or efficiency; subsidies, particularly with water; and retirement of agricultural lands with a severe drainage and toxic contamination problem.

It is estimated that these conservation and water efficiency measures could generate between 1.5 million and 2 million acre-feet annually by the end of the decade. Not only would that provide significant additional supply, but agreement on these conservation measures sets the stage for reaching consensus on Delta facilities.

Another opportunity to potentially free up considerable amounts of water for urban uses is renegotiation of the now expiring 40-year federal water contracts. Shortening the term of the contract and revising the price to more accurately reflect costs will encourage farmers to make different choices about the most economical use of water. Farmers will make economically-based decisions resulting in either increased conservation or voluntary transfers.

No discussion of the efficient use of water involving agricultural conservation would be complete without addressing the issue of ground water management. The current ground water overdrafting in many farming areas cannot be allowed to continue in the long-term. Therefore, there must be true, overall agricultural water conservation. It will not be acceptable to decrease use of surface supplies only to trigger increased ground water pumping, causing a greater overdraft. A program must be adopted to reduce the average annual ground water overdraft over the next 20 years. Innovative conjunctive use programs coupled with ground water aquifer recharging can be used to address this problem.

Further, although water marketing and voluntary transfers from agriculture to urban uses are viable elements of the efficient use component, caution must be exercised not to inadvertently fallow the most productive agricultural soils in California on a permanent basis. In particular, Class I and II soils (and other significant lands) should be regarded as valuable natural resources and should be protected from urbanization for at least the next two decades. If this position is adopted as policy for the state, then a sufficient amount of water must be retained for agricultural use to assure that the best soils can be successfully cultivated.

WATER BANKING FACILITIES

Water banking involves building surface and underground storage facilities south of the Delta to capture water during periods of high rainfall and huge runoffs when it is truly surplus to the needs of the Bay-Delta estuarine system. This water, by definition when adequate Bay-Delta protections and standards are enacted, would be excess to the ecological requirements of the estuary. Today there is not the capability of "banking" or capturing these surplus waters at peak runoff periods because adequate transfer and storage facilities simply do not exist. Now, pumping occurs on a more constant, year-round basis most years without the flexibility of regulating the pumping to the wetness of the year. With water banking, the pumps could be turned off during crucial months to increase spring outflows and to eliminate reverse flows when fish are spawning. This could be done without decreasing annual exports because the physical facilities would be able to capture the surplus water at other times during the year. The surplus water captured during wet months would also be higher quality, low in chlorides and virtually free of bromides. Further, there is a great likelihood that water banking will produce a new increment of water on the order of 250,000 to 500,000 acre-feet in normal to wet years. This can be done at the same time that environmental protections are strengthened. In this regard, water banking is the linchpin of consensus for both policy and plumbing.

Water banking is a non-isolated facilities proposal for improving Delta transfers by widening south Delta channels, strengthening levees, installing additional pumps and constructing Los Banos Grandes Reservoir and Kern Water Bank. Water banking is a superior alternative to the isolated transfer approach of a Peripheral Canal because it accomplishes the same objective without separating the incentives for southern California to protect the estuary from those of the Bay-Delta region. Unlike a Peripheral Canal or other isolated transfer facility, water banking maintains a non-isolated "common pool" of water in the Delta such that southern California and San Joaquin exporters have an interest in protecting the Bay-Delta Estuary in order to preserve the quality of water exported.

Proponents of the Peripheral Canal argue for an isolated transfer facility citing allegedly greater concerns about trihalomethanes (THMs) and earthquakes associated with a non-isolated through-Delta system. But close analysis of these issues neutralizes the arguments for a Peripheral Canal as a preferred engineering solution.

Trihalomethanes are formed when chlorine used in the treatment process combines with organic material in the water. Peripheral Canal promoters emphasize the organics in the Delta and gloss over the fact that the Peripheral Canal would be an unlined 43-mile channel, leaving water to pick up organics as it goes through the canal for storage in earthen terminal reservoirs prior to treatment. THMs are not eliminated with a Peripheral Canal and treatment processes must be installed that will remove THMs and meet anticipated stricter water quality standards, regardless of the kind of Delta transfer facility used.

Supporters of the Peripheral Canal also predict that some day an earthquake will destroy the Delta channel network, creating an inland salt water sea. They concede that such an earthquake would also damage a Peripheral Canal, but contend that an isolated channel could be rebuilt more easily than the Delta levee system. The problem with this argument is that it is based on the notion that we should abandon the Delta island levee system as we know it today and accept the eventual destruction of the Bay-Delta estuarine ecology. That is not a rational premise upon which to promulgate water policy.

It also ignores the function of the existing island levee system in maintaining an estuarine environment. The Delta islands and their levees are essentially "place holders" in the estuary, taking up space that otherwise would have to be occupied by fresh water in order to maintain an estuarine system. Thus, the Delta levee system has an important function in conserving fresh water. So, even with a non-isolated transfer facility scheme, the levees would have to be maintained unless it is the policy of the state to let the Delta Estuary become a salt water environment in the event of an earthquake. It is prudent ecological policy to reconstruct and maintain a strong levee system capable of withstanding severe seismic activity, regardless of whether an isolated or non-isolated transfer facility is advocated.

Faced with the persistent resistance to a Peripheral Canal, some leaders have suggested a "mini-Peripheral Canal" or small drinking water pipeline around the Delta. While this is less threatening than a full-blown Peripheral Canal as approved by the Legislature in 1980, this approach ignores the fact that the current export system is destroying the Delta and the status quo is not acceptable. So even if a mini-Peripheral Canal or pipeline were built, other facilities (such as water banking) would also have to be constructed to mitigate the negative impacts of the existing export system. The question then arises: Why not implement the non-isolated water banking approach and evaluate its operation before resurrecting the Peripheral Canal controversy again?

Water banking has the ability to enhance environmental protections, protect the fisheries with increased spring outflows and reduced reverse flows, improve water quality and increase the amount of water available for export in normal to wet years. It also has the distinct political advantage of providing a way to improve Delta transfer facilities with the least amount of opposition.

When consensus is reached among statewide leaders and organizations, the agreements should be implemented and ratified through a variety of mechanisms. Appropriate vehicles for institutionalizing the consensus agreements include: enactment of legislation (sponsored by the governor and written by a bi-partisan cross-section of the Legislature); ratification of the legislation and approval of any required financing by the voters in a ballot measure; incorporation of the plan by the SWRCB in the Bay-Delta decisions; voluntary agreements (such as the urban conservation BMP agreement); and amendments to the SWP and CVP contracts.

There are real opportunities for water policy consensus in the immediate future as outlined above. However, it should be underscored that California also needs a comprehensive, statewide growth management program that requires, among other things, that sufficient water supply be available before new growth is approved. It is in this context that the greatest consensus on water policy can be achieved.

CONCLUSION

California must have a reliable water supply to support its economic viability and there must be aggressive protection of the environment to ensure the Golden State's quality of life. These two goals cannot be met unless there is progress on meeting the state's future water needs. However, there will be no progress until statewide consensus is achieved on water policy.

In concept, the path to consensus for California water policy is relatively simple and straightforward. However, a simple concept should not be confused with an easy process. Stakeholders must be prepared to give up a little to gain a lot; they must negotiate in sincerity to assure a "win" for all sectors and regions of the state. The vital catalyst to achieving consensus is courageous and skillful leadership. If ever there was an issue in need of leadership, it is this. If ever there was a time, it is now.

CONSENSUS

Can the Theory Work
with Water?

As we have seen in the preceding chapters, none of the three main interest groups—agriculture, the environment and urban users—are unable to take significant action to meet their water needs. Each is, however, able to stymie the efforts of the others. The recent drought has pounded home the reality that this deadlock cannot continue if California is to prosper economically, environmentally and aesthetically.

In the past, backroom negotiations, legislation and lawsuits moved California water forward. These methods are no longer viable, not only because of the power struggle among the three main water interests groups, but because of a more informed and aware public. The time may be ripe for alternative methods of negotiation—consensus building.

Over the years, there has been extensive academic study of consensus and conflict resolution. There are several instances of water and land use disputes resolved through consensus efforts. Some of these successful efforts did not come together as formal consensus building groups; others were formally convened under the guidance of professional consensus facilitators. All of the groups followed the same general guidelines. Successful consensus centers around identifying needs rather than positions. It is the process of seeking agreements that address the interests of all the parties.

In the following essays, examples of successful consensus efforts are combined with an examination of what comprises consensus, according to several experts in the field.

CONSENSUS RESEARCH AND THE URBAN WATER CONSERVATION WORKGROUP: A CASE STUDY

Gala Argent

It's no secret that California's water conflicts take notoriously inordinate, often indefinite, amounts of time to resolve. Water decisions—bogged down by legislators constrained by regional differences, what many perceive as a recent past administration that did little more than coast with regard to water policy, and a system mired in regulatory and jurisdictional conflicts—most often end up being made by jurists after years of tying up the courts with expensive litigation. Because of this, water disputes, when they end at all, end with the legitimate needs of the various interests going unmet.

This is not to say that agreements are not reached outside of the court system. Deals have been cut, often by negotiators with an intuitive sense of what works at the bargaining table. The recent proliferation of "consensus" groups points to the need for alternacxative means of dealing with California's complex water issues. But only recently have some decision-makers begun to view the *process* and *principles* of conflict resolution as viable alternatives to court when dealing with water supply and allocation problems. Unfortunately, most California water leaders have been reluctant to rely on what they perceive as "touchy-

Gala Argent has reported extensively on California's water issues. She is president of Argent Communications Group, a marketing communications and public relations firm in Sacramento, and managing editor of *California Water Law & Policy Reporter.*

feely" endeavors to learn how to work through water problems outside of the court system.

Yet resolving conflict and building consensus have long been subjects of study in the academic realm, and a wealth of information and empirical data exist. Many academic disciplines—public policy, management, political science, psychology—deal with these topics, but the field of communications offers a particularly rich contribution to the research on conflict resolution.

What follows is an attempt to give credence to, and at the same time demystify, the conflict resolution process and to explore one situation where the process was put to use successfully, albeit unintentionally: the Bay-Delta Proceedings' Water Conservation Sub-group's efforts at Best Management Practices.

(Another organization, the State Water Conservation Coalition [SWCC], has operated parallel to and concurrent with the Urban Conservation Sub-group, with the same end result. Although both groups have wide overlaps in membership, the SWCC includes many elected officials and views conservation solutions as political, as well as technical. Here we focus on the Urban Conservation Sub-group's activities.)

THE BAY-DELTA WORKGROUP PROCESS

Begun in mid-1987 as a means to develop new water quality objectives for the San Francisco Bay/Sacramento-San Joaquin Delta Estuary, the Bay-Delta Hearing (later renamed the Bay-Delta Proceedings), conducted by the State Water Resources Control Board, has been the state's most far-reaching and consequential water decision-making process to date. Fraught with disagreements—legal and political, technical and rhetorical—among the disparate interests involved in the process, the hearing came to a virtual standstill following the November 1988 release of the draft Water Quality Control Plan. After considerable and vocal disagreement with the plan by water-user organizations, which felt it placed unreasonable restrictions on them, and by environmental groups, which wanted to see more protections for the Bay and Delta ecosystems, the plan was withdrawn.

As a response to that withdrawn draft plan, the State Board revised the scope of the proceedings. One of the revisions included the convening of workgroups. Said State Board Chair W. Don Maughan, "There was justifiable criticism of our 1988 report that we had not involved the parties as much as we should have in the hearing process, that we didn't sound them out as we went along. So, the workgroup idea was to open up the process and allow greater input in terms of interpretation of data and decisions on whether additional data are necessary."

As conceived by the State Board, the original objective of the workgroups was to identify areas of disagreement and sharpen the description of those disagreements for the State Board—not to put competing interests together to come up with mutually agreed-upon solutions. "We'd have liked for [solutions to have been developed by the parties]," said Maughan, "but I wasn't that naive to think that would happen. If that had been the case, they would have done so even before we got started. There's a real need to have that happen, but I didn't anticipate it happening."

To identify areas of disagreement, close to 20 workgroups and sub-groups were convened and have met more or less regularly for the past two years. Some workgroups have focused strictly on technical or operational issues, some have reached dead-ends and disbanded. But one workgroup in particular, the Water Conservation Sub-group of the Urban Water Demand and Supply Workgroup, flourished and has recently produced an end product that reflects consensus from its members, urban water suppliers, public interest organizations and environmental groups alike.

The sub-group's original agenda was to develop a process to more thoroughly evaluate or contest some of the assumptions that were made in the draft plan in terms of how much water conservation could be achieved. (The environmentalists felt that more water conservation could be achieved while the urban water suppliers believed the amounts were overestimated. But no one was really sure.) The sub-group began by evaluating existing conservation programs. Soon the concept of developing Best Management Practices (BMPs) became an objective. For the next year-and-a-half, details were worked out and in late 1991 a Memorandum of Understanding (MOU) was signed by participating agencies and organizations and delivered to the State Board to satisfy conservation requirements for the Bay-Delta Proceedings.

The end product, in effect, establishes an industry standard for urban water use. Two years in the making, the MOU consists of two components: water districts agree to carry out active conservation programs and, in exchange, public interest groups agree to support a reliable supply for urban water uses at the Bay-Delta Proceedings. The final product is not static, but takes into account that water conservation technologies and measurement methodologies will continue to improve and, as that happens, additional water conservation programs will be developed or numbers adjusted.

As part of the solution, a California Urban Water Conservation Council will be established to look at potential BMPs to be added to the list of BMPs and the parties who signed will be committed to following those programs. A schedule of implementation of active programs will be included and water agencies will have their allocations adjusted for the programs. If agencies fail to implement the programs, they will be short of water. The council will also receive an annual implementation report, analyze it and report the results to the State Board.

The sub-group's chair, Jonas Minton, chief of the Water Conservation Office at the Department of Water Resources, admits to looking at some, but not a lot, of conflict resolution literature in guiding the process along. Crucial to the sub-group's success, he believes, was that "the situation was ripe for a different approach. The past processes of initiatives, lawsuits and editorials have not allowed any of the parties to achieve their objectives."

After living through two years of the evolving process, Minton is sold on the approach. "I don't know of any other approach that has a greater chance for success for dealing with our water opportunities in California," he said.

THE ACADEMIC BASIS

Given that action is needed to cope with many issues revolving around water in the state and the ineffectiveness of the status quo, at the very least it is safe to say a new approach is worth a try. Any attempts at conflict resolution/consensus building with California's troubled water situation should focus on doing everything possible to enable the outcomes to be positive. The question then becomes: What factors can be said to predict or contribute to successful consensus-building or dispute-resolving efforts? Relevant academic research reveals several useful frameworks for addressing this question.

The concept of "principled negotiation," by which the parties reach agreement and avoid a struggle of wills by discussing the relative merit of *issues* rather than *positions* is the cornerstone of Roger Fisher and William Ury's *Getting to Yes, Negotiating Agreement Without Giving In* (Houghton Mifflin, 1981). "Principled negotiations," they write, "suggest you look for mutual gains wherever possible, and that where your interests conflict, you . . . insist that the result be based on some fair standards independent of the will of either side."

The authors contrast this method of reaching agreement with what they call "positional bargaining"—used by the Legislature and in the courts—in which each side takes a position on an issue, defends it and makes concessions until an agreement is reached. This method fails, they argue, by locking each side into its respective position; the more one defends a position, the more committed to it he or she becomes and the more identified one's ego becomes with that position as distinct from needs.

This way of negotiating is not only inefficient, they write, it also stands to endanger the ongoing relationship of the parties involved. An agreement, if reached at all, is likely to be viewed by both parties as unsatisfactory because the agreement becomes a question of which party has given in the most while legitimate concerns go unaddressed.

"Any agreement reached may reflect a mechanical splitting of the difference between final positions rather than a solution carefully crafted to meet the legitimate interests of the parties. The result is agreement frequently less satisfactory to each side than it could have been," they write.

Fisher and Ury illustrate the concept with a simple example of two students in a library: one wants to study with the window open, the other wants it closed. They negotiate back and forth about how much to leave it open, but no solution satisfies them both. Enter the librarian, who finds out what each side truly wishes to achieve: one person wants fresh air and the other wants to avoid the draft. The librarian solves the problem by opening a window in the next room, thereby meeting both parties' needs.

With regard to the Urban Conservation Sub-Group, initial meetings focused on trying to determine what amounts of water could be saved and therefore would have been deducted from the amounts urban agencies would be allowed to divert from the Delta. "Very quickly we recognized that was going to be a difficult, if not impossible process," said Minton. "So instead of looking at the numbers, we began by asking 'what are the demonstrated, reasonable water conservation programs.' We began a process of articulating what the participants' bottom line needs were."

Thus, the sub-group's agenda was directed from positions to needs, with the urban water users shifting their position from a firm number of acre-feet to the need for a reliable supply for their customers. Similarly, public interest and environmental groups shifted from the position of "no more water from the Delta" to the need to see that all reasonable and feasible water conservation programs were being actively implemented by the urban suppliers. And, advertently or not, one of the academic criteria of successful consensus building was met.

Other communications research has addressed the question of whether the phases of interactive problem-solving activities determine the effectiveness of those activities. A 1983 study by

Randy Hirokawa ("Group Communication and Problem-solving Effectiveness: An Investigation of Group Phases," *Human Communications Research* 9:4 [Summer 1983]: 291-305), assistant professor of speech communication at Pennsylvania State University, assessed whether "successful" problem-solving groups can be distinguished from their unsuccessful counterparts on the basis of the development of communications phases (such as "analyzes the problem" or "generates alternative solutions") in their activities.

Hirokawa cites the following four identifiable phases of interaction that are consistently identified by researchers:

Orientation, in which members of the group familiarize themselves with the problem, look at its parameters and suggest ways to go about solving it;

Problem-solving, where the group shares ideas and information and offers solutions to the problem;

Conflict, in which the group disagrees, criticizes and evaluates each other's ideas and suggestions; and

Decision emergence, where the group attempts to agree on an alternative, decide how it will be implemented and convince themselves it is the best alternative.

Hirokawa found no specific order of these phases to be uniquely associated with *either* successful or unsuccessful problem-solving. For the most part, the order of the steps did not matter to the outcome of the group's problem solving. He did observe a difference, however, which "appears to provide partial evidence that the manner in which a group approaches problem-solving may have important implications for that group's ability to come up with viable solutions to it."

Hirokawa observed that more successful solutions were generated by groups that had a full understanding of the problem before they attempted to solve it. "It appears that the 'successful' groups make an attempt to analyze the problem before attempting to search for a viable solution to that problem, while the 'unsuccessful' groups immediately begin working on a solution to the problem before attempting to analyze and understand it," notes Hirokawa. He suggests that groups which possess a better understanding of the problem before attempting to solve it arrived at higher-quality solutions.

Again, the Urban Conservation Sub-group fulfilled this criterion. Not only were the participants highly knowledgeable about California water issues going into the sub-group, they spent a significant amount of time early on exploring existing effective conservation programs before attempting to structure or direct solutions.

Finally, a study by Roger Pace ("Communication Patterns in High and Low Consensus Discussion: A Descriptive Analysis," *The Southern Speech Communications Journal* 53 [Winter 1988]: 184-202) sought to identify communication patterns that distinguish groups who reach agreement from those who don't. Among his findings was the pattern of terminating meeting episodes. Pace found that high-consensus groups consistently terminated episodes by voicing agreement for ideas, assertions or claims. Frequently, the voiced agreement occurred in episodes that were dominated by disagreement, but the group generally returned at the end to assertions that had previously won approval.

In contrast, low-consensus discussions contained very few episodes that ended in voiced agreement. Instead, group members would frequently end an episode by changing the topic or by making a new claim, which went undeveloped and unacknowledged by other members of the group. Episodes would also end by returning to ideas that had previously met with disagreement, thereby reintroducing conflict into the discussion, which then "escalated beyond its initial boundaries."

According to Pace, although the high-consensus groups had more agreement, a more important criterion of their success is "the sequence and distribution of agreement." High-consensus groups were able to "map" their consensus formation by voicing agreement at transition points. "By voicing agreement as the group ended one episode and started another, [they] were able to establish strong norms of agreement and progress toward overall consensus."

Again, processes used by the Urban Conservation Sub-group match those determined through research to be effective. The sub-group focused on areas of agreement rather than disagreement. After each meeting, the group would record, in writing, and circulate the agreements that been reached to that point.

APPLYING THE PROCESS

Some water leaders posit that consensus is not achievable, given the disparate positions and interests involved. But positive outcomes are possible at any level and facilitating such outcomes should be the primary concern of all of the players in this crucially important arena. Whether driven by governmental appointees, legislatively set-up planning bodies, or a handful of representatives of all major interests, the *process* should be applied. The alternative is the status quo of stalemate.

A strong mandate from the administration toward the use of such an approach, the assignment of representatives to participate and the assurance that solutions developed would be carried through would go far in ultimately producing a positive outcome from such consensus-building efforts.

Any water decisions should take public opinion into account. This public is aware. Recent public opinion surveys by the Field Institute and others point to an increasingly sophisticated electorate that is concerned with environmental preservation. It has been argued that the Department of Water Resources has the authority to carry through many of the controversial unfinished elements of the State Water Project. But, with the proliferation of the use of the initiative process, surreptitiousness is bound to result in problems.

Finally, California's various water interests must realize that fragmentation of the state's water problems does no good and much harm. Most currently believe that if only *this* group or *that* organization would back off and realize its folly, all would be well. Such a mind-set, which views loyalties to this or that faction as the highest good, divides. Rather, what is called for is an acknowledgement that all of California's often competing interests have contributed to the state's current water problems, and all can work to structure solutions.

The Urban Conservation Sub-group's Minton concurs: "Although conflict resolution may not have the highest chance for success, it seems to have a higher chance than any other that I can conceive of. The parties need to operate in good faith and send creative, articulate people to participate in these agreements. They must be able to listen to others and amend their views. If they go into the process thinking theirs is the only way it can work, the process is doomed."

None involved would argue that California's water problems are insignificant. But by viewing those problems as challenges to be jointly overcome rather than insurmountable hurdles, and by opening up to new and perhaps initially foreign approaches, solutions may be possible.

CONSENSUS BUILDING AT LAKE TAHOE

Geoffrey H. Ball and Barbara L. Stinson

INTRODUCTION

The "consensus building workshop" used in the development of the Lake Tahoe Regional Plan provides a textbook example of collaborative problem-solving (or consensus building) as an approach to conflict management in a difficult, long-standing, often bitter, land use dispute.

This chapter focuses on why the Tahoe situation was appropriate for consensus building, what was gained and at what cost, and what is transferable to other complex land use conflicts.

BRIEF HISTORY OF CONFLICT AT LAKE TAHOE[1]

The Lake Tahoe planning dispute goes back at least 20 years to the concerns of environmentalists over the increasing amount and intensity of development in the Tahoe basin. Lake Tahoe is one of the two largest alpine lakes in the United States that retains high water clarity and purity and great scenic value. In

Geoff Ball has worked as a master facilitator, trainer and conflict manager over the past 20 years.

Barbara Stinson is a mediator with the Keystone Center, a consensus building organization in Keystone Colorado. She specializes in natural resources management disuptes at the national and regional levels.

1950, 20,000 people lived in the basin; now more than 50,000 people live there. Many of these people chose to settle in Lake Tahoe to escape the congestion of urban areas and to have more personal freedom. This "frontier" attitude directly conflicted with the need to regulate development and human activities around the lake as the communities grew. More than 1 million people visit the basin either for summer recreation around the lake or winter skiing in the mountains that surround the basin.

The impact of development on the clarity of the lake was first noticed in the 1960s. Water clarity dropped from 120 feet in the 1960s to about 60 feet in 1985. This aroused substantial concern about severe and irreversible degradation of the lake's water clarity and its scenic quality. An organization, Keep Tahoe Blue (later, the League to Save Lake Tahoe) was formed to mobilize political support for action to protect the lake.

Lake Tahoe sits astride the border between Nevada and California. Early efforts to regulate development by each state acting independently showed the need for a bi-state regulatory agency. After substantial debate and one-on-one negotiations between then-governors Reagan and Laxalt, a bi-state agency, the Tahoe Regional Planning Agency (TRPA), was established in 1969 under a bi-state compact between California and Nevada. The compact was ratified by the U.S. Congress and signed by the president. Difficulties arose in implementing the compact, in part due to the voting rules of the governing board that allowed development to proceed unless blocked by action of a majority from both states.

These and other difficulties led to revisions of the bi-state compact in 1980. In 1982, environmental thresholds, such as lake clarity, vehicle miles travelled and air quality standards, were established in the compact to provide standards for future environmental conditions. The TRPA developed a regional plan to implement the compact, again with much heated debate and argument on the governing board and in the basin regarding its provisions. The plan was eventually ratified by the governing board. It was immediately challenged in federal court by the attorney general of the state of California and the League to Save

Lake Tahoe on the grounds that the plan was not sufficient to meet the environmental thresholds established.

Federal court Judge Garcia found in favor of the plaintiffs and in 1984 issued a moratorium on all construction in the Tahoe basin until an adequate plan could be approved by the governing board of TRPA. In response to the moratorium, the Nevada Legislature began to seriously consider withdrawing from the bi-state compact. Although the governor of Nevada promised to veto any bill suggesting withdrawal, the possibility of Nevada's withdrawal was real in 1985.

HOW THE CONSENSUS BUILDING APPROACH CAME ABOUT

At this time, TRPA's governing board appointed William A. Morgan as the executive director of TRPA. Morgan, who had been the regional forester for the U.S. Forest Service, was perceived by others in the basin as a person of great integrity, a fair-minded individual with good relationships with key individuals and extremely knowledgeable about Tahoe. This combination of qualities proved to be particularly important throughout the consensus building workshop.

Morgan proposed a consensus building workshop (CBW) to seek agreements that would meet the thresholds set by TRPA. He believed that a consensus building approach could be made to work, based on his training and experience in consensus building in the Forest Service. He had talked to nine key parties, such as the League to Save Lake Tahoe and the Preservation Council, and met with leaders in the Nevada Legislature. In these meetings he asked,"Would you be willing to join with me to create a consensus building workshop? We'll bring all the significant parties into Lake Tahoe to try to work out a plan that people can live with and that addresses all of the thresholds."

Morgan felt that the process must build working relationships between the people who were involved in the dispute or the agreement would not be sustainable. He believed that there was potential for on-going conflict at Tahoe and saw the long-term benefits in working through these conflicts. Morgan sought an agreement that would be binding for a 10-year period without substantial change to allow the agencies and organizations to operate under a consistent set of rules for a period of time, rather than continually fighting court battles.

Morgan then called in three different conflict management consultants: a mediator and two facilitators. Given his perception of the need for the parties to develop working relationships for future conflicts and to take responsibility for working through the dispute, he chose facilitation rather than mediation. Morgan felt that parties might shift responsibility for reaching an agreement to the mediator or might become dependent on the mediator to carry messages back and forth, rather than communicating directly with each other.

With the support of the key parties and the governing board, Morgan convened the first consensus building workshop (CBW) to address the complex, controversial planning issues at Lake Tahoe. In the Tahoe dispute there are essentially five categories of interest groups: development and property rights advocates, environmental protection and limited development advocates, local environmental agencies and commissions, local government and state and federal agencies. All key interests were represented in the workshop.

For about one year, the workshop met for two days approximately every three weeks. The group moved through the phases of consensus building described in this chapter. The CBW produced goal and policy statements that became the basis of the Tahoe Regional Plan that was subsequently adopted by the governing board. The acceptance of the plan by key parties led to the end of a court-imposed moratorium on construction in the Tahoe basin and brought about broader support for the TRPA in the basin.

CONSENSUS BUILDING—WHAT IS IT?

Consensus building is *the process of seeking agreements that effectively address the interests of the parties to that agreement, insofar as that is creatively possible.* At a minimum, consensus agreements are ones that people are willing to "live with." Ideally, in the context of public policy-making, the parties to consensus agreements will actively support that agreement in the formal decision-making process and through implementation.

Reaching consensus agreements among diverse affected interests is particularly important in situations where one or more of the parties can block or significantly delay implementation of decisions reached by an agency. Blocking might be accomplished by either working against the decision, through lawsuits and legislative action, or through opposition to a needed bond election or other implementation mechanisms.

There are nine typical phases of a consensus building process. These phases were followed fairly closely in the CBW process. As shown in Figure 1, they are:

Initiate the process: Gathering the key parties together in agreement to *explore* the use of a consensus building process.

Decide IF: Do we want to engage in this process?

Raise issues: Decide on a comprehensive list of issues that will become the basis of an agenda.

Design the consensus process.

Educate participants on the issues and "how to's" of a consensus-based process.

Work through the problem-solving stages: problem acceptance; problem perception, analysis and definition; alternative generation; solution formation; evaluation; development of recommendations.

Pursue formal decision-making: In this case, the governing board makes the decisions.

Begin implementation and follow-up: consisting of action planning, implementation and monitoring.

Maintain working relationships: Sustain the relationships developed throughout the process. Assure continued support and implementation of the agreement.

CONSENSUS   BUILDING

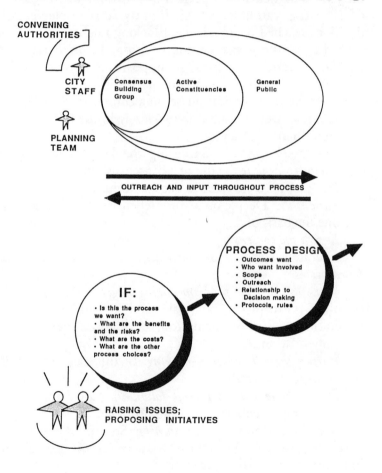

PROCESS

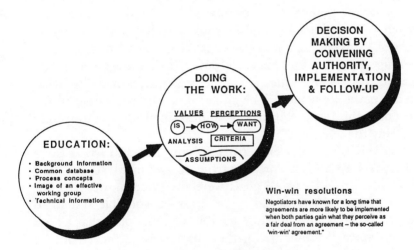

DECISION MAKING BY CONVENING AUTHORITY, IMPLEMENTATION & FOLLOW-UP

DOING THE WORK:

VALUES PERCEPTIONS

IS → HOW → WANT

ANALYSIS CRITERIA

ASSUMPTIONS

EDUCATION:

• Background Information
• Common database
• Process concepts
• Image of an effective working group
• Technical Information

Win-win resolutions

Negotiators have known for a long time that agreements are more likely to be implemented when both parties gain what they perceive as a fair deal from an agreement -- the so-called 'win-win' agreement."

People, process and substance

To the extent possible, we advocate first getting the right PEOPLE together. Then work out the understandings and ground rules with those people, and agree on the PROCESS (including ways to modify the process based on experience). Then begin to work on the SUBSTANCE.

Interests and positions

POSITIONS focus on specifics -- INTERESTS are more general, more like objectives. They lend themselves to collaborative work. Explicit interests allow more latitude to the parties in JOINTLY coming up with creative solutions or solutions that draw on the resources of all of the parties based on mutually acceptable agreements. Identifying interests allows creative negotiation based on a knowledge of others UNDERLYING needs and wants rather than having the negotiation become a test of who will push hardest for or hang on longest to a position.

APPROPRIATENESS OF THE TAHOE CONFLICT FOR CONSENSUS BUILDING

At the outset of the consensus building workshop, we informally assessed the likelihood of success using "Necessary Initial Conditions for Successful Consensus Building."[2] Each item on the list is considered significant by third parties involved in consensus building. The risks, if that condition is not met, are fairly apparent.

At Tahoe we informally used this list as a checklist, along with a list of potential "stuck places" to see where work was needed. On deficient items we took actions to improve that situation. Answers to these questions give a good review of the opening situation at Tahoe. (Note: While the questions are phrased as "yes-no" questions, the real question is "to what extent" is the item met.) The situation at the beginning of the consensus building workshop is described in the response following the questions.

Do INCENTIVES exist for resolving the conflict; is there sufficient URGENCY for all parties to get involved and stay involved? Not all parties' goals were the same, however, most parties agreed to two broad goals: create a workable system to protect the lake, and develop a stable regional plan that allows appropriate development. Further, parties were locked into a potential lose-lose conflict. Court costs were becoming a significant factor. The environmentalists had brought about a moratorium and knew they could hold it for a period of time. Yet, they could lose much more if Nevada pulled out of the bi-state compact. Everything that they had laboriously worked for would be without strong legal basis. They were concerned about damage to the lake's environment with the lifting of the moratorium. Parties supporting development knew the moratorium had hurt the local economy. The consensus building workshop potentially offered a way to find a solution that would enable owners to sell land at an acceptable price and allow revitalization of the local economies, particularly on the north shore of the lake.

Is the TIMING good? In the seventies, many developments were constructed. In 1985, there was abundant property for sale and a lack of pressure for development. Prior to CBW, the Nevada Legislature had just met and the pressure was on to reach an agreement before they reconvened in 1987. Morgan had just come on as executive director with the full confidence of the TRPA Governing Board.

Are positive and negative CONSEQUENCES known? Without an agreement, parties felt there could be both environmental damage and continued economic uncertainty that would prevent needed investment in the basin. As part of the early consensus building process, we went over the risks and benefits of the consensus building workshop. We reviewed other process alternatives—such as litigation—and contrasted them to the consensus building workshop. This helped participants conclude that, while uncertainties existed, there were no better process alternatives to address their interests and lead to stable agreements. (Later this conclusion became a touchstone. When things got terrible, as they did from time to time, when people saw no way out of the dilemmas that faced them, when they felt there was no give from the other side or sides, when tempers were aroused, when the process stretched out—it was this early work on the real process alternatives that people mentioned as they recommitted themselves to the task of creating the underlying agreements for the regional plan.)

Is there potentially a WIN-WIN situation? Enough ground had been covered in settlement conferences related to the moratorium to suggest that ways could be found to reach agreement that addressed the various parties' interests.

Is there a BALANCE OF SITUATIONAL POWER of parties? Each of the major players had a way of making the situation painful for the others; none of them could, acting alone, do the things they wanted to do or make significant moves toward their interests.

Is there a commitment by key parties to STRIVE FOR CONSENSUS? Three factors led the key parties to make their initial commitment to the consensus building workshop: the balance of situational power, Bill Morgan's leadership and the perception that the value of the consensus building workshop outweighed the risks when it was compared to other *realistic* alternatives. They knew that the workshop was costly in time and money, but most believed, or at least hoped, that the consensus building workshop could lead to a stable, lasting agreement that all parties could live with, that would, in fact, protect the lake.

Is there respected, competent and committed leadership? The broad respect for Bill Morgan and his personal commitment to the consensus building workshop opened the door for others to follow. The various members of the consensus building workshop brought a great variety of qualities and skills essential to this process—knowledge of the basin, personal contacts with key opinion and institutional leaders, persistence, a willingness to confront and to listen, creative conceptual abilities, knowledge of related law and legal history, negotiating skills—and many people provided leadership for the workshop at various critical junctures.

Does the process have the support of final DECISION-MAKERS? The governing board expressed confidence in Bill Morgan and, having tried other approaches, saw promise in supporting the consensus building workshop in its efforts.

Are all key parties included? In initiating the process, Morgan had identified those groups that needed to be included. At the initial workshop, other participants were also identified.

Is there a commitment to SHARING INFORMATION and direct communication? This developed over time. The initial work focused on building the confidence needed for participants to share information. Much of the information needed at the outset had been developed in prior efforts. Heroic efforts by the TRPA staff and many others kept the consensus building workshop supplied with the information it needed.

Is there a willingness to UNDERSTAND OTHERS' frames of reference? This also developed over time. The TRPA staff played a key role in providing basic information in an objective way—which had a secondary benefit of increasing the respect for the TRPA staff, due both to the quality of the work and building relationships with key participants. All participants were asked to read *Getting to Yes* by Fisher and Ury, with special emphasis on the chapter on interests.

Commitment of TIME and RESOURCES? Bill Morgan's commitment ensured TRPA's staff availability. The staff's commitment to the lake and the agency ensured the needed heroic efforts—like working seven days a week for extended periods of time.

What were the Benefits of the Consensus Building Workshop?

Near the conclusion of the workshop, the participants were asked about the benefits of the consensus building workshops. The benefits listed below were mentioned.

Broader understanding by the parties of the issues—The consensus building workshop educated all sides to the concerns and needs of others. Specifically, those concerned with economic development understood more about the environmental degradation; those concerned with the environment saw that a healthy economy could contribute resources to re-establish a healthy environment. This collective understanding allowed the development of a broad consensus that addressed both environmental and economic issues.

Better solutions, addressing the interests of all—Many new, creative solutions were generated in the discussions. For example, by staying focused on both the needs of homesite owners to sell their sites at a "fair" price and the needs of environmental representatives to protect the lake by not building on environmentally sensitive sites, the consensus building workshop reached a complex, workable and creative solution. This solution was based on ranking in environmental sensitivity all undeveloped lots, the transfer of development rights and a random drawing for building permits to develop market value for environmentally sensitive sites.

Energy mobilized to address the issue—The involvement of the parties in the consensus building process generated sustained energy over a long period of time. It focused attention on the critical issues. At the same time, the consensus building workshop

218   *Water Policy in California*

was strong enough to contain and focus the conflict in a productive way.

Lasting consensus among those involved—The consensus building workshop process developed commitment to the solutions that lasted through later stresses. Perhaps most important, the parties learned better ways to work through disagreements. They were thus able to resolve the conflicts that arose later in the implementation stages and during the final stages of the settlement of the legal challenges to the plan.

Acceptance of decisions—Participants in the consensus building workshop understood, through their involvement in the discussions, how each part of the package met the various parties' needs. Thus, parties accepted solutions that were not their ideal solution because they could support the whole package. This was particularly valuable in Tahoe given the complexity of the region, conflicting interests and pervasive lack of trust among parties.

A policy context for future specific decisions—Many felt that the consensus building workshop created deep understanding of issues which leads to sound policy level principles that can guide future decisions. The issues were examined with sufficient depth and thoughtfulness by all affected parties, so that the principles of policy could be translated into decisions.

Not all issues were resolved during the period of the consensus building workshop. And not all relationships were perfect. The completion of this phase of the work may best be likened to reaching a plateau—a place to rest, set up camp and from which to move on. As always with complex disputes, there was on-going work to be done. Members of the consensus building workshop continued to work together to develop ordinances implementing the policies and goals, maintain working relationships and sustain communication among the parties.

TRANSFERABILITY OF THE TAHOE CONSENSUS BUILDING EXPERIENCE

Clearly, parts of the consensus building workshop can be used in many situations. The "necessary initial conditions" can be used to assess a situation for consensus building and the transferability of the Tahoe consensus building workshop. Similar approaches have been used in reaching agreements on low-moderate income housing on vacant school sites, revitalizing a conflicted organization, developing recommendations for noise mitigation at a major airport, goal setting in large cities, increasing productivity in a major manufacturing organization and a variety of other settings.

Use of a neutral third party is particularly helpful in situations when no one is accepted by all key parties as having final authority, where there are many jurisdictions and/or large numbers of people involved, if the information is complex or technical and there is overt or covert conflict.

AFTER THE CLOSE OF THE CONSENSUS BUILDING WORKSHOP

The work of the full CBW wound down with the completion of the goals and policies. Yet much work remained. It took another year and a half to draft and approve the ordinances that implemented the goals and policies.

The governing board of TRPA did pass the plan produced by the consensus-building workshop, 13 to 1. The court lifted the moratorium; the community planning effort commenced; individual parcels were evaluated for environmental sensitivity. And, perhaps most importantly, the approach of using consensus processes became an accepted way of doing things at Lake Tahoe. Using a consensus building process, a redevelopment area in South Lake Tahoe was created with advantages to the environment, the economy and the aesthetics of that area.

Lake Tahoe before heavy development and recreational use took its toll. Through a consensus building workshop, conflicting interests were able to agree on a compact to protect the lake environmentally and allow controlled development. Photo credit: Water and Power Resources Services, U.S. Department of the Interior.

CONCLUSIONS OF THE FACILITATOR

Reflecting back over the CBW, some things stand out. People need a setting where they can talk with each other. During the course of this process, someone said, "You have no appreciation for how significant this meeting is. These people have not been in the same room together, talking civilly to each other, in the last five years." The fact that they could be in the same room, talking with each other about commonplace things, eating together, was very significant. In fact, many said that the most meaningful thing in the whole process was a barbecue.

Confidence building is important; it can lead to commitment of the parties to the process. Other key ingredients include evident leadership, exceptional staff support and effective functioning of working groups.

There needs to be an on-going mechanism for conflict resolution, a way for participants in the process to continue to contribute and to be involved in consensus building in future situations. The process must include efforts to keep the governing board involved and feeling that progress is being made.

Constraints on the process of inventing solutions did from time to time interfere with the progress of the CBW. For example, early in the process one party put forward a proposal that was strongly attacked by others. This party was then discouraged from offering a proposal in the future.

It would have been helpful for the facilitator to be involved beyond the narrow facilitation of the meetings, with more time spent learning the substantive details. For example, CBW members commented that they would have liked the facilitator to learn to "speak Tahoe" in order to make the meetings more efficient.

Economic issues could have been addressed earlier and time spent to find a safe way to do so. It was difficult to get economic considerations on the table. Understandably, environmentalists were concerned that substantial consideration of economic issues would give economic considerations equal standing with environmental concerns.

The program would have been expedited by a process management group to hold discussions on process outside the meeting time of the full group. Also, a computer with a group display would have been useful when all parties found it necessary to do detailed text editing.

Consensus building takes a long time when there are lots of issues to be addressed. Yet, a consensus process is often the only process that has sufficient staying power in difficult situations to struggle through to an agreement that will work and last.

NOTES

[1] A detailed history of this situation and the conflict is presented in "The Contribution of Consensus Building in Workshop to Regional Planning in Lake Tahoe" by Barbara Stinson, Massachusetts Institute of Technology, 1986. This same paper contains an evaluation by the participants of the consensus building workshop process conducted in 1986.

[2] We first saw many of these items on a list compiled by the Institute for Mediation by Jerry Cormick and Leah Patton.

BUILDING CONSENSUS ON CALIFORNIA WATER ISSUES: HOW IT COULD WORK

Robert Barrett

Let us assume it is now January 1994. The governor is about to deliver his State of the State address. During the past four years, California has made truly historic progress on water policies and practices, and the governor wants to highlight what went right.

A distinguished group of public policy analysts and dispute resolution experts is about to report to the governor about how such progress was achieved. They have interviewed a cross section of decision-makers in the state, have studied the various consensus building efforts undertaken in the late 1980s and have consulted with practitioners and academics in the conflict management field. Their charge was to look into the processes and approaches used to reach agreements and to come up with answers to some key questions: What techniques can help achieve successful policy results? What barriers to reaching such agreement can be identified and how can they be surmounted? How can decision-makers improve the efficiency and fairness with which agreements are reached, enhance the stability of policy outcomes and assure that wise policies are enacted, policies

Robert Barrett is an attorney, mediator and dispute resolution consultant. Currently, he is the principal partner in his own consulting firm, Robert Barrett & Associates, in Burlingame. He is a former program officer with the William and Flora Hewlett Foundation.

that take account of the best scientific and technical information available, that protect future generations and that can be adjusted as new or better information comes to light?

Here are ten highlights from their report.

1. TIMING IS CRITICAL.

The advisory group's first observation emphasized that the time for progress on California water issues was ripe by the early 1990s. Decades of advocacy in the courts, in the Legislature and through initiative measures had produced little benefit for any of the key constituencies (agricultural interests, urban water agencies, environmental organizations, business representatives, elected officials, outdoor recreation enthusiasts, commercial fishing interests, consumers and taxpayers). Huge amounts of money and time had gone into trying to influence policy-makers or to make policy choices, but virtually all such efforts had resulted in stalemates. Interest groups (singly or in coalitions) were strong enough to block action by their adversaries, but not strong enough to ensure that action was taken. By 1990, the frustration level was high enough that leaders of most of the principal interest groups were willing to try a new approach.

2. THERE WERE MANY SUCCESSFUL MODELS AND MUCH WRITTEN MATERIAL FROM WHICH TO GET IDEAS.

The water agreement group had the benefit of useful process ideas from other consensus building projects, both in the water area and on other topics. Past and contemporary projects to address water issues were followed closely in states as diverse as Florida, Hawaii, Idaho, Minnesota, Missouri, Virginia and Washington. The Water Code Roundtable in Hawaii, for example, was a useful model. That state had seen years of court and legislative battles over ownership of water rights under its prior appropriation doctrines. The battles escalated in 1978 with the approval of a constitutional provision that required Hawaii's state Legislature to protect, control and manage the state's surface and ground water. For nearly a decade, the state Legislature considered drafts of a state water code but was unable to enact one because of counterbalancing pressures from various interest groups. Finally, in 1986 an informal group of high-level water leaders, who were normally adversaries in court and before the Legislature, convened to clarify their differences and to provide a "safe haven" for discussion about where they might agree.

The Hawaii group, which came to be known as the Water Code Roundtable, began with three assumptions. First, some kind of state water code was inevitable. Second, an exchange of information and viewpoints by people who normally opposed each other had value. And finally, legislators might find the results of the group's discussions instructive in formulating a policy for the state. After awhile, it became clear that it did not matter so much who technically *owned* the water; the key issue was how water would be *managed* more wisely. The issues were: what should be meant by "wise management"; who should be involved in what kinds of decision-making; and how should critical determinations be made.

Facilitation of a dialogue in Hawaii thus eventually led into the mediation of an agreement on a state water code proposal. A consensus proposal was later enacted as a 75-page bill having three main parts: providing for water planning and coordination, establishing a system of dispute resolution that would channel disputes from the courts into an administrative process and providing for crisis management in times of emergency need. As an outgrowth of the legislation, a commission on water resource management was established to administer a system of water use permits.

The water agreement group in California also studied case examples of other consensus building projects in the state involving other issues. One such project involved growth management. For years prior to 1990, the state Legislature had wrestled with growth management bills, local electorates had faced initiatives to control growth, and citizens had grown more frustrated with perceptions of a decline in the state's "quality of life." Facing a range of complex choices and a number of conflicting bills on growth management, the Senate and Assembly offices of research decided to try a consensus building process that might help sort out key issues and produce a clearer picture of where the most effective policy tradeoffs might be made. The Center for California Studies at California State University, Sacramento convened a group of stakeholders consisting of 30 key representatives of the major interest groups on growth management issues. They met monthly from January through August 1991 to discuss a framework for possible consensus legislation and reported to a joint legislative hearing on Oct. 31, 1991 on the results achieved. In the process, participants clarified the numerous and highly complex diversity of interests at stake. They developed a number of useful approaches for making local decision-making more consistent with state policies; they outlined and then "fleshed out" potential policy agreements; and they worked to gain a broader understanding of the linkages among issues. Another outcome of the project was that its participants developed much improved working relationships, so that when legislative logjams later happened, they were able to steer their way out of stalemates.

The water agreement group also became familiar with some of the practical literature in the dispute resolution field. Four books proved particularly useful: *Getting to Yes*, by Roger Fisher and William Ury, which describes a process of interest-based negotiation that gave the consensus group simple, but highly useful, ideas that could guide their work; *Managing Public Disputes*, by Susan Carpenter and W.J.D. Kennedy, which presents step-by-step guidelines for managing a consensus building process; *Breaking the Impasse*, by Lawrence Susskind and Jeffry Cruikshank, which describes practical mechanisms and strategies for assisted negotiation; and *Getting Disputes Resolved*, by William L. Ury, Jeanne M. Brett and Stephen B. Goldberg, which suggests ways of designing systems of dispute resolution that can help cut the costs of conflict in the future. In addition, the water agreement group regularly kept up-to-date with developments in the consensus building field by reviewing the quarterly newsletter *Consensus*, published by the Public Disputes Network, part of the Harvard-MIT program on negotiation.

3. WHILE WORKING IN NEW WAYS, THE WATER AGREEMENT GROUP'S HIGHEST PRIORITY WAS TO ACHIEVE PRACTICAL RESULTS.

A key decision the water agreement group made early on, and that helped them repeatedly later, was to resolve to deal with both substantive and procedural issues in parallel. They recognized that by trying to formulate policy recommendations in a new way, they were sailing in unfamiliar waters. They encouraged innovative thinking but resolved to be constantly checking to make sure their course was working. The ultimate tests of every idea were: Will it advance our individual interests? Will it help us to discover common interests? Does it fit with the dynamics and needs of the group? Is the communication among interest group representatives clear and effective? Are we moving forward to generate better, more creative ideas? Will the approaches and techniques we are using give us better results than we could have expected from traditional means of public policy-making? Thus, by focusing on these questions, over time the water agreement group developed the capacity for examining its *process* issues in parallel with its work on *substantive* issues and correcting its processes as necessary.

4. THE FOCUS OF DISCUSSION WAS CONSTANTLY DIVERTED FROM POSITIONAL STATEMENTS TO DESCRIPTIONS OF WHAT INTERESTS EACH PARTY NEEDED TO HAVE SERVED IN ORDER TO AGREE.

Interests are the underlying concerns, needs and motivations of each party involved in a negotiation. Interests often must be probed for by asking "why?" when demands are made or positions presented. Interests are complex and varied. Some may be overlapping while others may be inevitably in conflict.

Generally, there are multiple interests involved in any consensus process and often many ways of satisfying them.

In the Hawaii Code Roundtable, for example, it became clear that the parties had common interests in finding wise and fair ways of managing water resources, although they had conflicting interests in ownership of water rights. The process began to make progress when the focus shifted away from their conflicting interests in ownership and toward their common interests in achieving sound planning and management of existing resources.

The stakeholding parties among the California water agreement group typically knew the often-stated demands and positions of each party so well they could easily parrot them. But surprisingly to many, they had had few opportunities to delve beneath the surface to understand why such positions were so vigorously propounded. Environmentalists, for example, found that agricultural interests were far from monolithic. The needs of farmers growing crops like cotton or alfalfa were vastly different from those growing food crops; those of small, family operations much different from large corporate concerns; and those of farmers in some geographic areas different from those elsewhere. Agricultural representatives discovered great diversity among environmental and urban interests, too. The highest priority for some was restoring fisheries, while for others it was securing improvement in the quality of drinking water. For others, achieving a balance that permitted economic growth was paramount. With a careful analysis of the large number of interests expressed by the stakeholding parties, many of which interests were held in common, it was easier for the water agreement group to agree on policies that had to be included in the state's policies.

Recognizing that there was a diversity of interests among many stakeholders, both within and between general interest groups, the California water agreement group used caucuses to identify and clarify both the differences and common interests among those "on the same side." This helped them tailor recommendations to a range of needs and interests and to be sure that all stakeholders' interests were addressed by any package of proposals.

5. THE GROUP STROVE TO INCLUDE ALL KEY STAKEHOLDERS IN THE CONSENSUS BUILDING PROCESS.

The results of a consensus process can only be implemented if all parties with a stake in the issue have "bought in" to the recommended solution. This means that all must be participants. For the California water agreement group, this did not mean that all were always present at the same negotiating table; indeed, many caucuses and technical meetings were held with only certain interest groups present. But there was a recognition that emerging agreements between a few needed to be negotiated with the rest of the interested parties before they could be included in any overall packages. One of the most helpful techniques for accomplishing this was to use a "single text" negotiating process, where a draft was produced that embodied the best ideas at the time, which was then circulated to all other parties for improvements again and again, until no further changes could be suggested that would make parties better off without making some party worse off than before. By stressing that the group wanted additional participants who could help improve the emerging agreements helped to assure that the water agreement group did not become an exclusive, but isolated, "in-group."

6. THE GROUP RESOLVED THAT PATIENCE WOULD BE REQUIRED AND WAS SATISFIED WITH TAKING SMALL, BUT STEADY STEPS.

Consensus facilitators often must urge participants to be patient and take the time necessary to fully understand the problem and the various interests that must somehow be satisfied if there is to be a consensus solution. There is typically a strong temptation to jump immediately into devising solutions before the problem has been fully explored. In the Hawaii Code

Roundtable, for example, and in the Water Conservation Coalition project, sponsors wisely invested substantial amounts of time and effort working on defining the issues, identifying stakeholders and clarifying key features of the issue and why different possible solutions would or would not work for all parties.

The consensus building efforts begun in the late 1980s and early 1990s on California water issues (including the State Water Conservation Coalition, the Three-Way Water Agreement Process and others) had made sufficient progress to demonstrate that a comprehensive approach was possible. Such efforts had also created a network of relationships among leaders who believed they could both work together and that they could rely on agreements that might be reached. Also, by the early 1990s the skills of consensus building were gaining greater acceptance as alternative dispute-resolution and conflict-management techniques because increasingly prevalent in courts, businesses, school systems, public agencies, nonprofit organizations and generally throughout communities of the state.

The initial efforts by the water agreement group toward a comprehensive and consensus-based process had wisely been slow and cautious. At first, they focused on understanding the range of interests that would have to be included in any agreement and achieving a fuller, and common, understanding of the complexities of the issues to be addressed. Then stakeholders spent considerable time patiently building frameworks for agreements, leaving details to be filled in later. In 1992, for example, a water agreement discussion group (including representatives of urban water agencies, agricultural agencies and environmental groups) reached consensus on a framework of principles that could guide the development of California water policy improvements. Later that year, the framework was expanded into an integrated package of provisions: general principles on necessary policy trade-offs, a series of specific agreements about procedures and operational guidelines to be implemented in critical areas, formation of task forces and monitoring groups to assess progress and identify areas of continuing discussion or study, and clear agreement on a continuing process for working out the numerous differences in viewpoint and conflicts that remained as new polices and practices were implemented. This approach paid off when new parties came to the table or as political developments threatened to overturn some earlier assumptions; the steady expansion of understanding kept progress on track.

7. THE GOALS OF THE PROJECT WERE FRAMED SO THAT ALL COULD HAVE A STAKE IN SEEING THEM ACHIEVED.

The water agreement group defined its goals as seeking to make unified and consistent what had previously been thought to be incompatible: protecting and enhancing environmental resources, improving water supply reliability for urban and agricultural users, enhancing drinking water quality, promoting conservation and wise ground water management, employing the best scientific information available, enhancing economic viability and remaining consistent with federal and state laws and regulations. While not perfect, agreements achieved along the way made all parties better off than they would have been with the traditional decision-making processes.

Participants in consensus building efforts defined their goals not as merely reaching an agreement, but as improving the way policies and decisions worked. Accordingly, they planned for monitoring of results. And perhaps most significantly, the representatives of all the organizations that signed agreements also agreed to continue meeting and working together towards further improvements and adjustments made necessary during implementation. Because of this commitment to *what worked,* not just *agreement for agreement's sake,* several better ways to enhance provisions of various agreements were developed and implemented, and new ideas could be tested and implemented if they proved successful.

Just as goals were framed inclusively, the water agreement group was careful to reframe issues not as either-or choices, but as searches for ways to satisfy all interests as fully as possible. Reframing helped to emphasize that the purpose of consensus building was to invent options for mutual gain. Win-lose, zero-sum solutions were de-emphasized. Instead, the group tried to invent as many options as possible on every issue, looking at the problems from a variety of different angles, asking "what if. . ." questions, looking for differences in value, probability and risk tolerance and time preferences. They separated the process of creating options from the process of assessing and prioritizing options or testing their feasibility. They never assumed "fixed pie"; rather, each party saw that by solving the other sides' problems, he could also help create value both for himself and all other parties.

8. TO KEEP A HIGH LEVEL OF TRUST, THE GROUP ALWAYS CONSULTED BEFORE DECIDING ON ANY MAJOR ACTION.

As much as possible, given the realities of time constraints, the water agreement group resolved to always consult every party before deciding on any major action. Even on minor decisions, the group tried to consult as widely as possible. They found that nothing helped build support for consensus action better than having each party be part of devising the plan for action. They created "buy in" and trust that each party's views would be treated as important and would be considered. Obviously, time constraints did not permit full-scale consultation on every occasion, and on some actions that were insignificant it would have been foolish and a waste of time to consult everyone. But the group developed norms that required the group as a whole to have a say in what actions would await everyone's input and which could be delegated to one person or a small group.

9. THE GROUP DEVELOPED A COMMON BASE OF UNDERSTANDING THROUGH JOINT FACT-FINDING.

The water agreement group created a common base of understanding on the scientific facts and technical issues by using a joint fact-finding process. One of the goals of the consensus-building effort was not just to reach agreement, but to make sure that the agreement was a wise and technically feasible, implementable solution to the problem. The foundation for such solutions had to begin with agreement on the facts and the science. The group used such techniques as hiring outside consultants jointly and developing a consensus set of instructions for research or technical studies.

The group also made regular reference to objective criteria for determining key factual assertions and when facing choices among different options. They found that arguments would be more persuasive and agreement more likely if based upon objective criteria. The group was constantly looking for fair standards and procedures. They posed each issue as a search for objective criteria that each party's representatives could successfully explain to its constituent organizations and to others. And they were open to reasoned persuasion about what criteria were most appropriate for any given situation.

10. THE GROUP RECOGNIZED THAT ITS PROCESS WAS PART OF A LARGER POLITICAL PROCESS WHICH WOULD DEMAND ENFORCEABILITY AND ACCOUNTABILITY.

Lastly, the water agreement group recognized that the negotiation process they were engaged in was embedded within a larger political process and that both had to be monitored. Many consensus processes have failed when they ignored the large political dynamics of the issue and focused entirely on getting consensus "around the table," leaving to chance the need for building consensus within the Legislature or Congress or within an agency. Large issues like water policy inevitably touch many interest groups that were not part of the consensus-building process directly. To assure that such groups would be supportive of the resulting agreements, the water group designed comprehensive measures for monitoring implementation and making adjustments if certain contingencies occurred. In effect, the group agreed to a set of contingency plans, so that consequence would be known in advance if rainfall levels were heavier or lighter than normal, or if other conditions affecting performance of the agreements occurred. The commitments made were always within the power of the parties to accomplish. They were also framed so as to be compliance-prone and clearly related to securing the parties' interests.

CONCLUSION

Looking ahead from 1992 at the work to be done to craft a sound agreement on California water policy, the task is daunting and may seem virtually impossible, particularly given the history of conflict, lawsuits, legislative and initiative battles, personal animosities, and diversity in cultures, lifestyles, resources and power among different stakeholding groups. But increasingly, around the country consensus groups—often "improbable coalitions"—have stuck with the process and made enormous progress. With major strides already taken by the California Water Conservation Coalition, the Three-Way Water Agreement Process and other groups, the scenario painted here may well be possible.

BUILDING CONSENSUS ON CALIFORNIA WATER POLICY

LeRoy Graymer

INTRODUCTION

Achieving consensus on water policy in California, if taken literally, suggests the attainment of a goal that seems illusory in light of the past decade. However, unless significant strides are taken toward that goal, the state may risk becoming immobilized in its efforts to accommodate increased demands on its limited and deteriorating resources. Doing nothing to overcome the deadlocks that seem to have built up around the existing coalitions and constituencies is likely to result in all constituents losing the capability to protect their real needs and interests.

Improved prospects for consensus may lay in the increasing evidence that deadlock is undermining the ability to satisfy many different constituents' real needs. In the language of those who work on consensus building process, "the Best Alternative to a Negotiated Agreement" (BATNA) may be getting worse! (*Getting to Yes: Negotiating Agreement Without Giving In*, Roger Fisher and William Ury).

Agricultural interests confront potential losses in their access to reliable and low-cost water supplies. Also, water quality

LeRoy Graymer is director of the Public Policy Program, University of California, Los Angeles Extension.

problems increase agriculture's costs of doing business and may threaten to limit its ability to maintain land in production. Water regulatory requirements create greater supply uncertainty and affect how agriculture will operate and what costs it will incur.

In political terms, agriculture feels that there is a lessening of their ability to have their voice heard with the same "clout" as in the past due to changes in the demographic and economic structure of our state.

Urban water suppliers and users see the dramatic growth in California during the 1980s and projected growth over the next several decades as substantially exceeding the water resources available for urban consumption requirements. With new facilities severely limited by political opposition and rapidly rising costs, the chances of bringing on significant new supplies are not promising. The water quality issue is a significant factor impacting supply and opportunities for conjunctive use. Ground water quality standards are under review and cleanup is very expensive. Loss of ground water that meets acceptable standards could reduce substantially the supplies in southern and central California.

Very large parts of urban water supplies for northern and southern California, as well as the growing urban sectors in the Central Valley, are highly dependent on water that flows through the Delta. The quality issues associated with that "water funnel" are key to these urban stakeholders, as well as the agricultural and environmental interests.

Environmental interest groups have, over the last two decades, gained support for protecting ecosystems and preserving water to help maintain habitats and aesthetic values. Increasingly, these groups have identified economic values associated with preservation and conservation to bolster the case for protecting water for environmental purposes. While the potential recognition of environmental values has increased, the ability to attain and preserve water resources for environmental purposes has been limited. It is easier to prevent action than to provide additional water for environmental protection.

This simple division of water interests into three cohesive groups is far from a full and accurate characterization of the water constituents in California. Not all interests coalesce around these three "cohesive" groupings. Indeed, it may be fortunate that this is not the case. If there is any hope for consensus approaches to water issues in California, it is precisely because there are opportunities to seek out mutually supportable options that cut across interest group boundaries.

The recognition that no one set of organized interests has the power to achieve important goals by exercising clout, or by consistently winning "real" victories in court, increases the likelihood of negotiating consensual approaches. In many cases, the *only* alternative to negotiated settlements is stalemate or, possibly worse, an erosion of the ability to satisfy real needs of the constituents identified by broad interest group categories.

Before proceeding with a discussion of consensual approaches, I must emphasize that these strategies are *not* substitutes for the governmental and legal processes. Legislators and governors have always played the central role in bargaining and negotiating among competing interests. What is making it harder for elected officials to successfully negotiate water policy strategies is the difficulty of reconciling regional and other divisions which have become so factionalized. This difficulty is further exacerbated by the fact that there are fewer resources to use in accommodating diverse interests. Negotiations generally work most easily when political leaders are distributing "shares" in a growing economy and an abundant resources base. As the issues become more and more a matter of imposing constraints and allocating or reallocating limited resources, the policy process is more readily deadlocked. Another impediment to developing consensus results when historically competing interests have developed stereotypical perceptions of their adversaries. Negotiations depend on hearing nuances and listening carefully for opportunities to attain mutual gain from newly developed approaches. If people speak from battle-hardened positions staked out over time, dialogue is then used to dispute the opponents' arguments and further the rationale behind fixed positions. This situation is characterized in the consensus literature as "positional bargaining."

Unless a process is employed which moves these groups out of the "fighting arena" and affords the opportunity to frame the discussion in such a way that new information can be introduced and new options and strategies explored, there is little chance of breaking these deadlocks or configuring solutions that do better than "splitting the difference."

Assuming that this analysis is reasonably correct for at least some of our major water policy debates in California, what advice would one offer to political leaders?

Simply calling for political leadership in situations where the political risks appear to far outweigh the chances of success in bringing about new policy initiatives seems unfair. The history of the last 10 to 15 years provides pretty conclusive evidence that without some realignment of political interest or some extraordinary efforts to forge new coalitions, the consequence of "assertive leadership" does not promise much success. Without a realignment of perspectives or consensus effort, one would predict that political leaders will look for other policy issues to demonstrate their ability to lead.

Given the water battles fought throughout the 1970s and 1980s, some fairly strong "positions" have been carved out by all major parties. The key to negotiation strategies is to find ways to help groups sort out "positions" from "needs." "Positional bargaining," as it is characterized in the negotiations literature, is best designed for fights in the courts. The adversarial method of getting to the "truth" is deeply embedded in our legal system. The democratic process of negotiating among diverse interests is more familiar to the work of our legislative bodies and between legislative and executive branches. When political parties were stronger, they played more powerful roles in negotiating differences among competing interest groups.

Water policy in California may have evolved into the mode of single issue politics which is less congenial to bargain and trades. The orientation of getting something on this round and in turn giving something in a subsequent round is based on a view that, on the whole, you are better off to keep your "adversary" in the game as a potential partner in another round. If the lines become so tightly drawn that regional, urban, agricultural and environmental interests are consistently opponents, stalemate is most likely.

If we want to break out of this gridlock, we need activities that provide political leaders some leeway to return to a bargaining style of politics and policy-making for California water policy. The following outline of principles can help move the process of water policy development toward working collaboratively to develop creative solutions.

One of the first issues to decide is whether the consensus building approach should be employed to devise an overall water policy strategy or to encourage negotiation efforts to resolve specific disputes. The argument for a grander approach is based on the view that ultimately all major roads or "canals" lead to or disseminate from the Delta. Unless some broad-scale plan that resolves these differences is developed, efforts to work out specific disputes or issues will either fail or be insignificant.

The contrary view is that some successes in using consensus to resolve more limited disputes will demonstrate the value of opening more dialogue among diverse interests. This is a more incremental approach to building trust and confidence in dispute resolution processes for formulating California water policy.

It can be argued that a combination approach of encouraging specific negotiations and undertaking a broader consensus building approach is desirable. Since political leaders must make their own decisions based on better knowledge of the political landscape, this discussion focuses on some principles to follow if the leadership should choose to pursue consensus and negotiations approaches for larger and/or more limited water issues.

PRINCIPLES TO HELP GUIDE NEGOTIATION AND CONSENSUS BUILDING PROCESSES

A. Initiating the Process

The section is suggestive of questions to be addressed even before making a decision to pursue consensus building options.

1. The likelihood of such efforts succeeding, particularly for larger-scale policy consensus building, is greatly enhanced by a strong mandate from the state's top political leadership.

2. This approach must be consonant with an overall style of leadership from the governor.

3. A carefully designed process must be instituted to ensure that a facilitating entity and the custodians of the process do not have a hidden agenda to promote. The participation of high-level representatives is needed, but the process is more likely to succeed if it is facilitated by a non-stakeholding neutral party.

4. Representation in the process must be inclusive of all major interests and key policy makers to ensure fairness and to ensure that any agreements reached will be supported by the constituents of these various groups. This *may* mean selecting some diversity from each of the various constituents' interests.

Also, it is probably necessary to be concerned about regional as well as interest balancing. Furthermore, the inclusion of some groups not strictly reflective of water interests can help, e.g. the League of Women Voters, as well as trade or business interests without ties to specific water issues.

5. The process should be launched by political leaders who can express their commitments to this activity and demonstrate a strong interest in its success. A willingness to be kept apprised of the group's work with an eye to receiving its product as guidance for concrete policy actions is important to ensure meaningful participation. Some direct representation from state political leadership may be advisable.

Construction of the Los Angeles Aqueduct to conduct water from the Owens Valley to the Los Angeles area generated outright battles in the early 20th century. Photo credit: Los Angeles Department of Water and Power.

B. Once the Process has Begun

1. The cardinal rule of such a process should be that each participant will set forth *needs* as opposed to *positions* and justifications.

2. In turn, participants must be prepared to *listen* to others' real needs as opposed to arguing positions. In fact, it is useful to see if people can try to give voice to what they are *hearing* from others. One function of the group's facilitator is to assist individuals and the group to sort out real needs and to enhance listening skills.

3. This part of the process should be structured to produce a single agreed-upon document identifying the real water needs of the several interests. Ideally, this document will reflect a realistic assessment, not just a wish list.

C. Inventing and Identifying Options and Strategies

The search for options and strategies to achieve or satisfy diverse needs is at the heart and core of consensus building. Often, consensus building or negotiating is perceived as finding an acceptable *compromise*. Ideally, a good consensus process develops mutually supportable options that provide better solutions than splitting differences.

While illustrations can be risky, the following examples demonstrate how such an approach might work. Proposals for developing new California water facilities provide a good example of how discussions have broken down among the various interests. However, if new storage and/or conveyance facilities are tied into firm protections for environmental values and could enhance efficiencies or permit greater conservation at reasonable costs, there might be broader support for certain kinds of facilities proposals.

Another illustration is borrowed from the land use policy field. Environmental protections or mitigations in a different location are provided as an offset for some opportunities for development in the initial area in question. (Transferable development rights have been employed for this purpose in land use disputes.)

Here are some guidelines for the options development phase.

1. Provide a brainstorming opportunity away from the day-to-day arenas where each word is measured politically. Do not debate each idea at the initial stage—get as many options on the table as possible.

2. Be systematic in developing ways to evaluate options against the needs statements developed earlier.

3. Create explicit criteria for judging among options: e.g. costs, political feasibility, ease of implementation in light of institutional barriers, who may be impacted, outside the stakeholder?

4. Identify information and analysis required to make the assessments of options.

5. Engage in joint fact-finding to obtain information required to make assessment. Use expertise when necessary.

6. Be sure to have participating stakeholders keep in touch with their constituents to evaluate acceptability of options. It is important to have periodic reality checks with the key policy-makers. This is best done by having ongoing representation from those offices from the outset.

7. Because this is a process that can drag on for a very long time, it is important to have timetables set by the group. If progress is occurring but more time is required, the group can negotiate new timetables. The political leaders may want to initially set or help prescribe a timetable.

8. Finally, if the process can produce some agreements, it is essential to devise an implementation plan to ensure that the group's effort does not get lost.

CONCLUSION

It is important to reiterate that these processes are not meant to be substitutes for the role of elected officials. The function of these consensus building efforts is to provide an arena free of the day-to-day advocacy environments where an attempt to break out of deadlocked positions can be explored. If the impetus to employ these processes comes from political leaders, they may succeed in building potentially constructive coalition opportunities and introducing some more flexible options for developing new water policy options.

If these approaches succeed, leaders have a better chance of having followers. If they fail, the political risks to leaders may be less than in trying to push ahead on an agenda when there is not adequate political support.

ACHIEVING CONSENSUS ON WATER POLICY

Robert T. Monagan

The biggest problem that confronts California today is not water, but water policy. From day one, the historic battles in our state over who was to get the water were ferocious, but in the broadest sense were at the very least resolved temporarily.

Plans for diversions, storage and distribution were developed and carried out. But in our present condition and circumstances, plans are not the immediate answer. The major question, and one that must be addressed initially, is that of creating a "water policy" for the state.

Californians for Water (CFW) has undertaken a new and different approach in attempting to build consensus among warring interests to achieve just that—a water policy that would precede agreement on any plan to accomplish that goal.

Obtaining an agreement in these days on a state policy on any subject is most difficult. In our changing, growing, fractured society, any public policy achievement is hazardous. To be successful involves an approach rarely tried and one without absolute assurances for success. But old, standard approaches towards acceptance of any public policy do not seem to work either.

Robert T. Monagan is president of Californians for Water and chairman of the California State World Trade Commission. He is a former speaker of the Assembly in the California state Legislature.

Why not? There are at least four different forces at work in our society today that dictate an unusual approach to reaching some accord on water policy and plans for California. They are forces that apply equally to other major public programs and make public policy creation a difficult task at best.

SPECIAL INTERESTS AND POLITICIANS

First of these is the manner in which special interest groups have grown, with a narrow focus on questions and the ability to create powerful support mechanisms for their issues. On any current issue, these special interest groups can stimulate significant public concern over any proposal to solve a public policy and block any action.

We now have a plethora of interest groups, on every side of every debate, with sufficient muscle to kill or delay proposals. None on their own, however, can create sufficient support for acceptance of any suggestion.

All of these interest groups may have worthy objectives, but many times they have a life of their own. The number one objective is to continue to create controversy so that financial and volunteer support will continue and grow. That is not necessarily an unworthy objective, but when problems are complex and controversial there is no consensus device available to bring these divided groups together.

Harsh divisions of interests and needs is prevalent in the history of water development in California. Water, it seems, is to be fought over. The rising tide of potent special interest groups compounds modern-day efforts to resolve the issues.

These harsh divisions of interests and needs for water do not lend themselves to any easy solution in the public or political arena. That leads to the second concern.

There was a time when the Legislature could give direction and leadership to resolve an issue such as the present water dilemma. Major water plans were pursued and resolved, largely in the legislative arena.

It is my conclusion that when society is divided into a number of strong and vigorous special interest groups, such as those that divide us on the water questions, even the strongest of political leaders finds it difficult to respond to the challenge. This is not a putdown of our politicians. When issues are divisive or difficult and there is no consensus or agreement among the contending parties, politicians dive for cover.

Even the very best legislators find it unpleasant and politically unpopular to take the lead on issues where the questions divide us 51 percent to 49 percent. These conditions are even worse for the politician who is primarily motivated to re-election. Unfortunately, opinion on most public issues is divided along such narrow margins. It is one reason for stalemate and why there has been a rising tide in the use of the initiative process.

Politicians are much more comfortable when nearly-resolved proposals are presented to them and they do not need to battle with interest groups or a narrowly divided public response. Before we land too hard on politicians, we should note that these perverse conditions are just as common in the private sector. Splintered opinions and interests exist there, too.

The third factor is the rapid growth and changing demographics of this state. This factor relates with the rising special interest group phenomenon and political vacuum. This growth and the ethnic and economic diversity that accompanies it impinges on the public policy resolution process.

Although a great number of Californians are disinterested in public policy questions, other than having someone provide them with transportation, education and water, there is a large bloc of citizens who not only want these governmental services, but want to be part of the process of determining how services will be provided. If these citizens are not part of this decision-making process, they are less likely to give support to their legislative representatives or to support ballot proposals that need their votes. Unless they or their leaders are participants, they are less likely to be supportive.

Sherman Island in the Sacramento-San Joaquin Delta is part of the complex Delta system that is of such fundamental importance to the California water system. Photo credit: California Department of Water Resources.

CALIFORNIANS FOR WATER

It is under these circumstances that Californians for Water was formed. Many water leaders, who had been laboring over the issues for a long time, concluded that even if they were successful in reaching technical consensus, a broader-based group would be required to gain acceptance for those conclusions. The factors discussed here, along with other conditions which needed to be recognized, dictated a new type of organization and process. The conclusion was reached that a new decision-making mechanism would be required if we were to reach any consensus.

It must be involving by design, be inclusive by direction and build consensus from the bottom up and not the top down. In a sense, we needed to start at the end to get to the beginning. This process caused great suspicion and skepticism. It was not the usual organizational approach. But we are optimistic that this new process of involvement will bring results.

Formally organized as a non-profit corporation, CFW has a group of directors who represent a cross-section of the interests in the water battles, as well as broad public interests. The board directed the convening on an initial "Water Policy Council." One hundred people were assembled to discuss what was needed to build consensus and create a water policy/plan for the state.

This assembly was a reflective representation of California. There were people representing agriculture, business, labor, environmentalists, fish and wildlife, government, north, south, urban, rural, Bay Area, mountain, Delta, men, women, Asians, Hispanics, African-Americans, water interests and non-water interests. It was a microcosm of the state.

Members of this very diverse group were somewhat startled when they arrived at the meeting. In many instances, they were among strangers or long-time antagonists. They were most startled when they were confronted with no agenda. Without an agenda, CFW was trying to dispel the concern of many who believed that there really was a "hidden" agenda and that somewhere along the line they would be asked to support some predetermined conclusion.

Those attending were asked to help develop an agenda. This is not to suggest that there was little thought about what might be the ultimate conclusions of the convocation. It was hoped that the involvement process would contribute to a better understanding among the participants about the water problems of the state, and that at the very least they might "agree to agree" that these problems had to somehow be resolved in the best interests of all Californians.

It was also hoped that this carefully selected but representative group might agree to continue the collective efforts of CFW. In addition, if sufficient confidence was reached within the group, there could be discussions of the essential elements of a water *policy* and not a *plan*.

The discussions ultimately led to an outline of the essential requirements for a water policy that would: a.) satisfy the needs and requirements for all future Californians, extended out to some future date like 2010 or 2020; and b.) make the state economically sound and as environmentally attractive as possible.

It is safe to say that progress has been made; it is not safe to say that success is assured. There continues to be a growing atmosphere of trust, understanding and recognition that water is a major component in determining what kind of future is in store for the state. Will all future Californians, as well as the present large population, have the kind of jobs that will be required and a desirable environment in which to live?

Californians for Water will continue its efforts to reach accord on the water needs and desires of the state. It is hoped that in the near future agreement can be reached on a water policy. If this threshold can be successfully crossed, then it will be possible to develop an action plan that would meet these objectives.

The primary thrust of Californians for Water is to help build the support necessary—among the interest groups, the government and the public. We anticipated that this would be one of the major roles that CFW could play.

To some, it appears that there are now a number of other efforts attempting to resolve the water needs and differences among users. Some are afraid that CFW activities are interfering with the progress of other groups. CFW does not see it that way, does not believe that there is any incompatibility, nor any hindrance by or to others by these parallel efforts. We believe that they all are part of the necessary dialogue and discussion that can lead to agreement.

There is a great deal of consensus effort going on between three major parties—agriculture, environmentalists and water providers—to resolve the Delta dilemma. An agreement in this process would be the key—and perhaps most essential—component of any policy and plan for the state's water. There appears to be no way to solve either environmental or water use concerns without a Delta solution.

The governor and his water experts are also bringing leadership into the process. The Legislature and Congress have proposals that may ultimately play important roles. Local governments have established domestic water conservation programs. All of these efforts clearly indicate that there is a strong sense that now is the time to resolve our differences and reach an accord that will provide all of Californians with the water required to meet all purposes.

Optimism and encouraging developments should not cloud our vision about the difficulty of arriving at the best policy for all Californians. Any conclusions that are agreed to must represent changes in the way water is used, shifting some priorities and accepting compromises and conditions that are politically tough.

But we can be optimistic as well as realistic. There is too much at stake. The economic and environmental consequences of taking no action are too horrible to accept. We are running out of time. We must proceed swiftly, but not at the expense of outrunning our ability to achieve consensus. We must find a resolution to how we use water and how we can assure a necessary supply of it to meet our requirements.

Every Californian—present and future—is at risk until we resolve this critical issue.

THE STATE LEGISLATURE:

Can It Solve the Problem?

Legislators agree that it is time for action on California water. To some, however, "consensus" is just the newest buzzword. Any piece of successful legislation or negotiation can be considered the result of consensus—groups coming together to give a little to get a plan they can live with. They point to several significant incremental developments over the past few years, in addition to the major earlier negotiations that built the State Water Project.

In acknowledging the need for a new water ethic, there are several components that many legislators agree must be included: water conservation and recycling; water marketing; environmentally sound water development; ground water management; Delta protection; growth management. Solving the problems in the Delta is almost universally regarded as the number one priority. Many look at traditional water facilities as a last resort.

As these legislators explore the colorful and contentious history of California water, they examine what worked and what didn't, the reasons for success and failures, and actions for the future.

CALIFORNIA WATER—MYTHS, FACTS, REALITY AND THE FUTURE

Jim Costa

THE IMPORTANCE OF WATER RESOURCES TO CALIFORNIA

The history of California is very much the history of agriculture and water development, from the small irrigation projects built by the Franciscans, to the formation of the first irrigation districts (in Turlock and Modesto) in 1887, to the massive federal Central Valley Project (CVP) and the State Water Project (SWP). Water development has allowed California, an essentially semi-arid state, to grow to the world's sixth largest economy, with agribusiness one of its prime and most vital industries.

Annual agricultural production in California approached nearly $20 billion in 1991, a spectacular achievement in light of the state's unprecedented drought and sufficient to ensure its continued position as one of the premier agricultural areas in the world. Farming and agricultural-related employment account for one out of every five jobs in the state and for nearly one-half of the work force in the San Joaquin Valley. In addition, California

Assemblyman Jim Costa of Fresno was chair of the Assembly Water, Parks and Wildlife Committee from 1983 to 1990.

agricultural exports, which amounted to approximately $4 billion in 1989, are one of the few bright spots in the otherwise rather dismal national balance of trade situation.

The success of agricultural production in this state has enabled consumers to enjoy an unparalleled variety of food and fiber products at consistently affordable prices. Californians are better fed and clothed than virtually anyone in the world as a result of the hard work and dedication of this state's farmers.

In recent years, however, this industry, which has been so critical to the development and economic expansion of California, has been faced with an increasing number of seemingly insurmountable problems that directly threaten its future survival. Those problems include urban development pressures, issues related to agricultural drainage, air quality, international marketing and trade, the current drought and limited water supplies, depleted ground water supplies, and the need to address environmental concerns related to fisheries, wildlife habitat and recreation.

Perhaps no single issue facing California today is more controversial or more complex than the proper stewardship of the state's water resources. Within the larger question of state water policy is the supply and demand issue, which requires that policy-makers and water planners satisfy the diverse needs and sometimes competing values of people, industry, water quality, fish and wildlife, recreation and aesthetic needs, as well as agriculture.

Unfortunately for the citizenry of this state, some political leaders, rather than responding to the need for concerted and thoughtful long-range planning in this area, expediently argue that any shortages simply should be made up by arbitrarily taking water from the rural farming areas. Needless to say, that approach will prove to be extremely disruptive to the agricultural segment of our economy and it is not, in fact, the solution that adequately resolves this issue.

I, as well as many others, believe that we can provide sufficient water supplies to meet all of the state's needs without jeopardizing one segment of society in order to satisfy the needs of other segments. However, it is going to require a cooperative and conciliatory attitude and good planning techniques and appropriate management approaches.

MYTHS AND FACTS CONCERNING WATER RESOURCES IN CALIFORNIA

A number of unfounded myths and false perceptions have been fostered, particularly in recent years, concerning agricultural water use in California.

Myth #1: Agriculture uses over 80 percent of California's water supply.

Critics of agriculture like to perpetuate the myth that agriculture uses over 80 percent of all the state's water. This is an inaccuracy that is frequently perpetuated by the media. The actual number, when the total volume of the state's water is taken into consideration, is nearer to 30 percent. The 80 percent figure represents agriculture's share of the state's developed water; that is, water which is made available for society's use through various man-made facilities such as dams and aqueducts. But that, in fact, is really just a fraction of the water that nature actually provides.

The state has an average annual run-off of 75 million acre-feet. (Run-off is defined as the amount of water which falls on the state in the form of rain and snow and runs off into the streams and rivers.) Of that 75 million acre-feet, 63 percent or 47 million acre-feet is undeveloped. It remains in the stream and river system for the benefit of fish and wildlife. When this issue is viewed in that context, agricultural water use in this state is not exorbitant (just over a quarter of the water provided by nature), particularly in light of how dependent we are on the food and fiber it produces.

Myth #2: There is not enough water to meet the state's needs.

Most, if not all, areas in California have adequate water supplies in normal and above-average rainfall years to satisfy the demands of both urban dwellers and agriculture. The state Department of Water Resources (DWR) estimates that urban water demand is expected to increase very significantly, over 30 percent, by 2010, which is attributable to the large growth in the state's population. Currently, California is adding about 750,000 new residents annually. During the same period however, DWR anticipates no increase in net water use by agriculture as a result of continued efficient irrigation techniques and little expected expansion in farmland acreage in the state.

The real problem lies with providing adequate supplies to meet our needs in dry years or during times of drought. However, I am convinced that if we use our water supplies wisely and efficiently, even during periods of shortages we will be able to meet all our needs into the foreseeable future. In order to provide adequate supplies for all sectors of society, we must pursue a variety of compatible development and supply management strategies, including offstream storage, small water project development, ground water banking, conservation and recycling, voluntary water transfers and conjunctive use of ground water and surface waters.

Myth #3: Farmers waste water.

It is very easy to cast a critical eye on water use by agriculture if that examination is only superficial. Certainly, we cannot quarrel with the need to scrutinize the use of water in these severe water-short times, whether it be by farmers or city residents. No use of water which is inherently wasteful should be condoned. However, it takes a great deal of water to feed every man, woman and child in this state. Various studies estimate that the amount of water needed to produce the food consumed by the average person for one year is 1.5 million gallons.

And consider just these two facts. First, unlike urban water users, farmers have virtually no discretionary use of water. For farmers, there is a direct relationship between how much water they apply and how much produce the ground will yield. Second, farmers are allocated only so much water each year. When that supply is exhausted, there are no additional supplies. Now, what could be a stronger incentive to use water efficiently than these two factors?

Perhaps no other single use of water has been more closely analyzed than that of water used by agriculture. Government, the academic community and private research organizations have conducted seemingly endless studies of this issue. And contrary to the criticisms of agriculture, these studies demonstrate California farmers to be very efficient in their use of water.

Myth #4: Virtually all of California's water problems can be solved by taking water from agriculture.

It is simplistic, unrealistic and just plain unfair to suggest that we can solve California's water problems simply by restricting the flow to farms. We need to discard the notion that we will solve our water problems by penalizing the people who produce our food and fiber.

Agriculture is dependent on reliable supplies of water for irrigation. Reductions in those supplies would cause economic havoc throughout the Central Valley and would affect a wide range of people, from the local farm implement dealer to the grocer to the schools, in countless communities. The economic implications of taking water from agriculture would spread statewide and reverberate even throughout the national economy.

Those who tout taking water from agriculture probably have simply not thought through the consequences. If we lessened supplies to California agriculture by 10 percent, for example, we could water more lawns and landscape, fill more swimming pools, supply more fountains, take longer showers and bring millions of new people into the state! More water for urban areas would cause water quality to worsen, air quality would further deteriorate, overcrowding would increase, traffic gridlock would be more prevalent and open space would dwindle.

Myth #5: Water is the only resource in California that is subsidized and California farms are run by gigantic corporations.

The policy of providing certain financial guarantees as it relates to water resources is, of course, not an isolated example of government subsidization. Government provides funding assistance and strategies to many programs to encourage the success of some public benefit or ensure the widespread provision of vital goods and services, such as abundant and affordable food and fiber products.

In California, less than one-third of the state's irrigated farmland is supplied with subsidized water. Farmers in this state have entered into various long-term contractual agreements for water deliveries with both the federal and state governments. So-called water subsidies apply only to land receiving water from the federal water supply system, and those recipients must agree to limit the size of their farms. All other farms pay full price for their water allocations.

According to statistics from the U.S. Bureau of Census, the size of the average California farm is some 369 acres, which is nearly 50 acres less than the national average. In addition, nearly one-half of California farms produce annual sales of only $10,000 or less. And among those farming operations that exceed this figure, over 80 per cent cultivate fewer than 500 acres.

DISCUSSION OF WATER ISSUES OVER THE LAST 10 YEARS

It seems that using the term "consensus" has come into vogue recently, but anything that is successful in terms of legislation or administrative action was successful because a consensus was reached—everyone had to compromise a little in order to get something accomplished. After all, consensus does not mean that everyone agrees on every point, but that enough people agree on enough points so that some movement is made.

While politically we have been at a stalemate over the last 10 years on major water development projects and potential Delta transfer facilities, a number of incremental achievements have been realized. These achievements address water supply and quality, fisheries, water conservation and water marketing issues. Some of the more significant developments:

* The Legislature enacted the Urban Water Management Planning Act of 1983 and the Agricultural Water Management Planning Act of 1986 which require large water suppliers to prepare water management plans.

* The Coordinated Operation Agreement (COA) was signed by the U.S. Bureau of Reclamation and the state DWR in 1986

and concerns the coordinated operation of the CVP and the SWP. The COA will provide for more efficient operation of the two systems and secures the involvement of the CVP in meeting state water quality objectives.

* Several bills have been enacted by the Legislature to encourage and facilitate voluntary water transfers and water marketing. In early 1991, when the fifth year of drought seemed to be reaching a crisis point, the governor called the Legislature into "Extraordinary Session" to deal with impending severe water restrictions on household use, loss of permanent agricultural crops and the possibility of extinction of various fish species. The most significant result of this special legislative session was the creation of a state drought water bank which secured nearly 800,000 acre-feet of water through voluntary transfers from farms in the Sacramento Valley and the Delta.

* The Legislature enacted a number of bills to protect the quality of our ground water supplies and to confirm the authority for the state to build ground water storage facilities south of the Delta as part of the SWP.

* Measures were approved to restore fisheries and to authorize the State Water Resources Control Board to consider stream flow requirements in applications to appropriate water.

* Legislation was enacted to protect Delta levees and to plan for continued water exports in the event of levee failure.

* Proposition 65, the Toxic Enforcement Act, was approved by the voters in 1985 to protect drinking water from harmful chemicals.

* A myriad of bond laws were enacted to provide loans and grants for safe drinking water, wastewater treatment, water conservation, agricultural drainage, ground water recharge and fisheries restoration.

* The Suisun Marsh Preservation Agreement was signed to protect the Suisun Marsh, which is a critical feeding and resting area for waterfowl on the Pacific Flyway.

* An agreement was signed by the directors of DWR and the Department of Fish and Game (DFG) which identified steps needed to offset adverse impacts on fisheries caused by the SWP.

* In 1984, the Legislature authorized construction of the Los Banos Grandes offstream storage reservoir as a facility of the SWP.

* DWR is proceeding with development of the Kern Water Bank project which will store ground water for the SWP.

However, in spite of the incremental progress that has been made to address the state's water problems, it is clear that the three primary interest groups—agriculture, environmentalists and urban dwellers—still harbor many concerns regarding current state water policy. Urban dwellers are concerned with the quality of their drinking water and with adequate supplies for comfortable living. Environmental groups want past wrongs righted—fisheries must be restored and the Delta must be protected. Agriculture is afraid that their water rights will be diminished and their water taken away. The drought has heightened this anxiety because growers took cuts of 100 percent from state supplies in 1991 due to the drought. In addition, industries other than agriculture are beginning to feel the economic effects of continued dry years and the lack of reliable water supplies.

One of the reasons for lack of progress is a fundamental difference among these groups over the question of growth. Do we allow unlimited growth and try to keep up with the water supply? Or do we somehow limit or control growth to stay within our water supply means?

WATER POLICY FOR THE FUTURE—CONSENSUS BUILDING

The Sacramento-San Joaquin Delta, which is the source of drinking water for 19 million Californians, is clearly the key issue which must be addressed in meeting water supply needs and addressing water quality problems. The Delta levee system is threatened by floods and earthquakes. A failure of levees could result in drinking water that is too salty for consumption. Delta waters are degraded by agricultural runoff and industrial effluent. Water quality is also affected by organic contaminants from Delta soils, thus causing concern that proposed drinking water standards may not be met. Fisheries have declined from historic levels.

Over the last 10 years, two major legislative packages addressing comprehensive water policy were proposed and failed. The defeat of the governor's water package in 1984 was the genesis for formation of the Committee for Delta Resources Improvement to address the Delta and San Francisco Bay. The committee attempted to open the avenues of communication between traditional interest groups who have been on opposite sides of water development issues.

Frankly, we were tired of fighting over fixing the water transfer system in the Delta, and losing, while the Delta continued to deteriorate. We hoped to overcome past mistrust. We felt that we could not continue to progress without the type of physical facilities in the Delta that would enable the SWP to operate more efficiently and mitigate its impacts on the fisheries and water quality.

The facilities portion of my legislative package included dredging and widening channels to allow for improved circulation. A new channel would be built if engineering studies proved that the channel work would be insufficient to solve the fisheries and water transfer problems that exist in the Delta. Construction was prohibited from commencing until DFG and DWR entered into an agreement to implement measures to prevent or offset any impacts on the fisheries.

Unfortunately, my package failed because of lack of support from key southern California and San Francisco Bay Area legislators who succumbed to the fears of the environmental community. Environmentalists felt that the package did not contain enough protections for the San Francisco Bay and Sacramento-San Joaquin Delta. They demanded protections that water development interests could not agree too, including mitigation and restoration of fisheries to historical levels.

There are two schools of thought on how to develop consensus and proceed with resolving our water problems. One school has to resolve the big question of the Delta through a consensus building process. Another feels that an incremental approach is the only way to make progress. I think we should pursue both concurrently and, in fact, many consensus building efforts are working today.

A good example of incremental consensus building is the effort currently underway pursuant to my Assembly Bill 3603 (Chapter 1068, Statues of 1990). This legislation formally established the San Joaquin River Management Program and Advisory Council and Action Team to identify measures to improve the conditions on the San Joaquin River and to balance all beneficial uses—flood protection, water supply, water quality, fisheries, wildlife habitat and recreation.

Some of the key elements which exist in this process and which must be present in any consensus building process are:

a) A formalized process must be established. Whether through executive order, legislation or some other process, a politically legitimized process will provide the impetus for all parties to participate in the process and to take the task seriously.

b) The process must be all inclusive and must not exclude any individual or interest group. All affected local, regional, state and federal agencies must participate, as well as water users and environmental organizations.

c) Meetings must be open to the public and invite public participation. Public education must be emphasized.

d) The process must have the support of political leaders.

e) Identify goals in which all interest groups will receive some benefit.

While these elements may be useful in any consensus building process, they certainly do not guarantee that a consensus will be reached on a major issue such as how to address the problems of the Delta and whether to build a Peripheral Canal.

The major players must be willing to recognize the political clout of the strong environmental movement and must be willing to address the environmental problems caused by past water projects. Each of the three interest groups—environmentalists, agriculture and urban areas—must recognize that each group individually has the power to stall any efforts they are not satisfied with. Urbanites, as well as agriculture, must admit that they have dammed and polluted rivers and destroyed values and wetlands. Everyone must agree that they are part of the problem and are responsible for sharing in the solution.

WATER: A CHALLENGE AND AN OPPORTUNITY

Phillip Isenberg

[Editor's note: Sometimes humor is helpful in the state's heated discussion of water issues, as Assemblyman Isenberg's memo shows.]

The document reproduced on the following page, labeled "CONFIDENTIAL," was found by a staff member of Assemblyman Phillip Isenberg (D-Sacramento) at a copying machine on the sixth floor of the State Capitol. A handwritten note (on the next page) was also found.

A spokesman for Gov. Pete Wilson indicated that the governor had no knowledge of anyone by the name of "Milo."

Assemblyman Isenberg represents the Sacramento, Antioch and Lodi areas in the state Legislature. He chairs the Assembly Judiciary Committee and has been a member of the Water, Parks & Wildlife Committee for nine years.
No information could be obtained on "Milo."

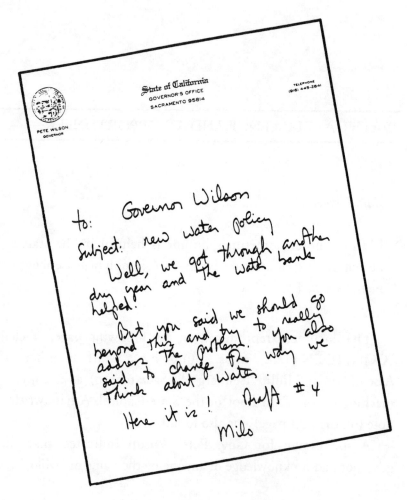

State of California
GOVERNOR'S OFFICE
SACRAMENTO 95814

TELEPHONE
(916) 445-2841

PETE WILSON
GOVERNOR

to: Governor Wilson

Subject: new water policy

Well, we got through another dry year and the water bank helped!

But you said we should go beyond this and try to really address the problem. You also said to change the way we think about water.

Here it is! Draft #4

Milo

[Recommended speech for Gov. Pete Wilson:]

WATER:
A CHALLENGE AND AN OPPORTUNITY

Let me start this morning by telling you how proud I am of how Californians have responded to the state's drought. Californians conserved more water than anyone could have expected, and we were able to turn a potential disaster into a blueprint for dealing with the state's water problems.

When I took over as governor of this great state in January 1991, we were in the middle of a fifth year of drought, a drought that affects almost everyone: from farms to cities, from north to south.

When I took office, it was a relatively easy decision to get the state involved in the drought—and get involved in a big way. And with your help we met the challenges of the drought through a series of innovative water management strategies, cooperative arrangements between water users, highly successful conservation programs and, yes, I'll admit, a little bit of luck.

I directed the state Department of Water Resources to organize a "state water bank" to ensure that areas that were in desperate need of water could obtain the supplies they needed. The success of the water bank astounded us all. Water was shifted from areas of surplus to areas of need.

We worked in Congress to secure approval of a $30 million drought relief package, and we moved a $100 million drought relief package through the state Legislature.

The Department of Fish & Game was out drilling wells to ensure there was enough water for our wildlife—for the ducks and geese and swans that use the waterfowl areas in the Central Valley. We made sure there was enough water in the streams so fish would survive the drought, too.

We encouraged strong water conservation measures on farms and in cities—and the results have impressed us all.

But maybe the most important thing we did was to make sure that there was enough water in reservoirs to guarantee human health and safety should 1992, God forbid, also be dry. But our job is not done. Mother Nature *could* deal us a sixth year of drought, and each year of drought will make it more difficult to avoid widespread economic and environmental damage.

It would be short-sighted for us to view periodic droughts as the only water problem we have in the state. And it would be likewise short-sighted to suggest only emergency steps to face this drought—ignoring the long-range water problems of California.

Political history, conversely, suggests that any governor should pause before offering anything like a new approach to water. Since 1960 all attempts to make major policy moves have failed. And this is the dilemma we face today:

* As we concluded the fifth year of this drought, major urban areas experienced cutbacks in water supplies and a growing number mandated water conservation.

* Key areas of the state (particularly coastal California) are not linked to federal or state water projects and are most susceptible to periods of drought.

* Agriculture, while largely substituting ground water for reduced water supplies, cannot continue to do this endlessly. Besides, the increased cost of underground pumping is substantial.

* Our population is growing and it demands and needs more water. By the year 2015, our state will have 10 million more people than today.

* The easy dams—the economically efficient projects—have already been built. What remains are mostly expensive, inefficient and environmentally damaging projects that no one is prepared to finance.

* The federal government won't finance new water projects. The consequence of this retreat is to compel Californians to bear the full cost of new projects. As a result, we have been forced to re-examine old proposals in the face of new financial realities.

* Our environment—justifiably—is becoming more and more important. Substantial environmental damage is occurring

daily because of the drought: fish populations are way down; water quality in our rivers has suffered; and the wetlands areas that house ducks, geese and other wildlife have declined even further. The challenge for us is to take this new water reality, adjust it in an era of financial constraints and commit ourselves to satisfying the real needs of the citizens of this state: personal, economic and environmental.

One thing has struck me about the water debate—indeed about so many public debates over controversial issues—we only see our fights and failures, and success is ignored or taken for granted. But positive steps *have* been made over the last decade. Even as I speak, representatives from business and industry, agriculture, municipal water suppliers and environmental groups are negotiating sensitive water issues with the hope that California's water future can be decided by consensus rather than by conflict. If they are successful, all of California will be better off.

And while my administration continues to monitor these discussions—and I encourage them to continue—we need to move forward with a water policy to meet the current drought and lay the foundation for solving California's water problems.

WATER CONSERVATION AND WATER RECYCLING

First, water conservation and water recycling, which by necessity will get us through this drought, are needed over the long run to help meet the water needs of a growing state.

As I mentioned earlier, our recent conservation efforts have been outstanding. I'm also pleased by local efforts to pursue making fresh water from the sea—desalination—and I encourage these efforts to continue. In addition, the state Department of Water Resources has been key in negotiating a major, new urban water conservation plan—a plan that will forever reap benefits.

But we need to see similar heroic efforts in agriculture, which uses more than 80 percent of the developed water in the state. It is incumbent on agriculture to have a goal of at least 10 percent permanent savings in place by next year.

My administration will continue to monitor these conservation efforts to ensure that they become a *permanent* part of our water future. We can't afford to save water during a drought only to go back to wasteful ways when the rains return.

VOLUNTARY WATER MARKETING

Second, voluntary water exchanges between agricultural and urban areas must be encouraged and promoted.

Earlier I mentioned the tremendous success of the "state water bank." By putting a modest economic incentive into water policy, we found that more water could be freed up for health and safety purposes. The water bank must continue—on a permanent basis—with changes to make it work even better. Assemblyman Richard Katz, for example, has a bill in the Legislature that deals with this issue, and my water advisors are working with him on this important matter.

As part of these negotiations, I have asked the director of DWR to review all state water marketing laws and to work with the Legislature to design new legislation to update these laws. We need to make sure that these efforts minimize the economic impact on rural areas and that we protect our fish and wildlife resources, as well. But even more needs to be done.

WATER DEVELOPMENT

Third, rational and enviromentally sound water development will play a necessary role in the future.

During the Deukmejian years, the state moved ahead on two major water projects—the Los Banos Grandes Reservoir and the Kern Water Bank—that will allow us to "bank" water in wet years as insurance against dry years. These projects, when completed, will represent more than a billion dollar investment in our water future.

Water banking makes greater use of the high flows through the Sacramento-San Joaquin Delta by diverting water during the winter and storing it south of the Delta for use later in the year.

These projects also will improve the drinking water quality for most Californians, as well as help fisheries in the north and water quality in the Delta and San Francisco Bay.

Many of my water expert friends argue that water banking south of the Delta won't work unless we build a Peripheral Canal—or altered version of the canal—to allow us to divert more of the high winter flows. But what they don't seem to understand is that by insisting on a new Delta water export canal as a condition for building these south of the Delta storage projects, they doom these projects from the start.

Let's face it, the history of water in California is a history of mistrust. Until we honestly move to solve fishery and water quality problems in the Sacramento-San Joaquin Delta and San Francisco Bay, it's irresponsible to suggest that more water should be shipped south.

As many of you know, the federal Environmental Protection Agency has stepped in to say the state has not done a good enough job to protect the state's environmental resources. The newly created Cal-EPA is working closely with the federal EPA to put together a plan that protects our environment and provides enough water for our cities and farms. And that's why today I placed a moratorium on increased water exports from the Delta—except for emergency drinking water needs. I also have sent a letter to President George Bush asking that the federal government comply with this moratorium.

But a solution to the Delta's problems will not come by itself. The Resources Agency secretary, Doug Wheeler, will begin discussions immediately with the various water players throughout the state, including the federal government, to negotiate a moratorium agreement that will allow water quality and fish experts to fix the environmental problems of the Delta area. But there is more in this state that needs to be done.

TOXIC DRAINAGE

And, fourth, we need to deal with toxic drainage problems that are fouling our drinking water and environment.

We know of the problems at Kesterson Reservoir: agricultural water tainted with the natural chemical selenium in toxic amounts. The water sits in toxic ponds and continues to poison, kill and deform waterfowl. This has to end.

Yet selenium is only one part of a complex array of drainage problems that result from bringing water to naturally dry lands and irrigating them for agriculture. Selenium, pesticides and simple salt are the most serious threats to the health of agriculture in California today.

And we must solve this problem. By "we" I mean all of us— north and south, rural and urban, farmer and environmentalist.

Although I am aware the voters are suspicious of major new spending programs, I am convinced that they will support a well-balanced plan to protect the quality of their water supply— protect it for the environment, for drinking water and, yes, for agriculture as well.

I will prepare and lay before the voters a plan for agricultural drainage clean-up that ensures the safety of our water supply. But in exchange for a major commitment of public monies the taxpayers must be assured that the common good during and after the drought will be served. And I suggest to you that by helping agriculture find a solution to its drainage problems, we should expect reciprocal assistance in meeting the demands for new water for growing urban areas. My previous discussion of water marketing suggests a merger of interests—agriculture's drainage problem, urban area needs for assured water supplies and the use of conserved water to protect the environment—may lead to productive results.

A final word and let me close. I know it will take only a few minutes after I finish for the naysayers, the doubters, the tired warriors of the water battles of the past, to say "no, nothing can be done." But if California is to succeed in the 1990s, it will be because we build new coalitions. And isn't it time to do that?

We have built more than 1,200 dams on 800 rivers in this state. And, for the most part, they have served us well. We enjoy the benefits of water storage, power production, flood protection and recreation. But society has paid a price. We've lost forever a valuable part of our natural heritage: fisheries have been eliminated in some places, merely devastated in others; more than 90 percent of our wetlands habitat has been lost; wild rivers have disappeared; the numbers of wild birds, ducks and other animals have declined dramatically.

The past, build-at-any-cost policies are no longer acceptable. We are one state, yes. But if we're to share the bounties, we must also learn to share the pain. I believe that California can move forward on water issues. But we need to make the hard choices. We need a water revolution in this state that means more than fighting the old fights and dredging up peripheral canals that are dead politically and dead economically.

I'm prepared to move forward with a new water ethic—a water ethic that promises people more than water rationing, drought crises, environmental destruction and expensive new projects. The time for reaction is in the past; we can no longer face water problems with either a southern or a northern perspective. We need a California perspective. Thank you very much.

Assemblyman Phil Isenberg speaks on water issues at the 1989 Water Education Foundation Executive Briefing. Also at the table are former Department of Water Resources Director Bill Gianelli and Water Education Foundation Executive Director Rita Schmidt Sudman.

CALIFORNIA WATER RESOURCES

David Roberti

I believe water to be the most pressing issue facing the state today. The drought underscores the painful reality that we must reform and reassess the management of one of our most precious resources. This drought has introduced a new and important political variable into the water debate because all sectors of society are affected. This factor mandates that all players are involved in the debate and that whatever solution is proposed will entail some pain for everybody. There must be sacrifices by all parties so that our diverse state can benefit from a sensible, comprehensive and long-term water policy.

California has a colorful history surrounding water. It has never been a subject where the interested parties seemed especially moved by warm good fellowship and sympathetic generosity. History books and folklore reveal that this was not the case during the hydraulic mining wars or during the early disputes between Miller, Lux and the other water barons of the great Central Valley. The colonization of Owens Valley by Los Angeles and the war of the peripheral Canal—or the war of the Non-Peripheral Canal two years later—were not distinguished for their harmonious public and private debates.

The one brief shining moment in recent water history came in 1960 when enough folks moved from their hardened positions

Sen. David Roberti (D) is president pro tempore of the California Senate and a member of the Agriculture and Water Resources Committee.

to come together and approve the state's water project. Most experts, in hindsight, ascribe this to Gov. Pat Brown's brilliant leadership, agreement from most interested parties and complete silence from the still prenatal environmental movement. Even so, the state project was approved by a bare majority of the voters.

History reveals a painful record of drought for our state. Rainfall history, established by tree ring studies, shows that California had a drought that lasted from 1755 to 1825—70 years of continuous dryness. Precipitation never came up to the long-term average during that entire period. We had another drought that lasted 20 years, from 1865 to 1885. It put most of the land grant cattle ranches out of business, probably setting off the biggest real estate deals in California history.

As far as we know, these droughts were not the result of global warming. They were part of the natural weather pattern. They make the state's current dry period, or even the great drought of the 1930s, seem like a blip on the radar screen.

It is possible that we are now in year six of another 50 year run of dry weather. If the water supply system fails to work during this drought, or comes close enough to failing, then we will probably have reached a point where enough people will be scared enough to find some reasonable common ground to move California water policy forward.

But this raises two crucial questions. Under what conditions will it be accepted that the system has failed to work? And if it fails to work, which way is forward? I don't claim to have evangelical answers to these questions, although it wouldn't hurt. But I do have some thoughts about them.

First, the drought adds a political necessity factor that should create enough urgency to lubricate the creaking, grudging, lock-up of political forces that has kept water policy from change for a long time. This is not to slight things like the Kern Water Bank, the Imperial Irrigation District negotiations or the few other evolutions of that sort.

Second, this sets the stage for some serious experimenting with water policy. Things like water trading and banking and water conservation, especially agricultural water conservation, are recommended by many different groups. And, for every group recommending a proposal, there is a group critical of that proposal.

However, we don't really have a lot of experience with how well these suggestions might work in practice, so the discussion has stayed mostly in the higher reaches of interstellar rhetoric. With luck and reasonable good will, maybe we can use the grim reality of drought to improve the quality of our debate about long-term water policy. There is a range of topics that I believe must be included in any comprehensive water policy.

WATER TRADING, BANKING AND PRICING

From this predictive point of view, one of the most interesting of the governor's drought proposals was his directive to the Department of Water Resources (DWR) to create a water bank to lubricate water trading. Water trading has been discussed for several years now and the Legislature has passed several bills intended to encourage trades. But we haven't seen a lot of action.

Then the governor asked DWR to make some trades happen. I am not unaware of the controversy that this decision produced, particularly among the agricultural sector. Regardless of the efficacy of the water bank in 1991, it gave us something that we needed—real-life experience.

Water trading is an essential field for more activity. To work, it will take considerable cooperation from the State Water Resources Control Board to ensure that traders' long-term water rights are not somehow confounded. It will also take some cooperative restraint from the environmental folks. They have a slight tendency to favor water trading, especially as an alternative to building new water projects, but then they object to the actual transfer of water from one place to another on environmental grounds. While there certainly is room for some thoughtful exercise of judgement about the environmental consequences of trading, water trading isn't going to build a very positive reputation if every proposed trade leads to knee-jerk reactions and lawsuits.

If more trading proves fruitful, then a logical extension in future years would be development of water contingency contracts. Places that needed really reliable water, and were willing to pay for it, would contract with places that could tolerate interruptible water, as long as they were paid for the possibility of disruption. The contracts would run long-term, but would provide for water transfer only in very dry years.

Potential receiving areas would pay a small retainer each year and a fairly high price for water that they actually got in dry years. A system of contracts of this sort would help cushion the impacts of future drought, would make them more predictable and would be economically beneficial to farmers. I suspect that these water insurance contracts would be a good idea even if we somehow substantially increased the overall supply of water.

Water trading is really just a mild way of reforming water pricing. A fair case can be made that the roots of California's strenuous debates about water lies in the irrational way that water is priced. This is a large subject with a long history and there is not space to rehash it here. But there is enough truth to the argument that I can promise that it will not just go away.

One last observation about water trading. Maybe it won't work. If so, "why not?" will matter a lot. If it doesn't work because farmers and maybe even an occasional urban area with abundant water rights unreasonably refuse to play, even though they would be well-compensated for their trouble, then there may need to be a statewide response.

WATER CONSERVATION

Drought is also the mother of conservation, in the same way that poverty keeps the poor from squandering the wealth they don't have. As a longer-term policy, conservation is a major component for all parties. In particular, we have all heard the argument that if only agriculture, which uses about 80 percent of our developed water, would conserve a little, then the urban areas would have plenty of water for a long time. This idea has won a lot of adherents in the last year or two.

Going from the simple arithmetical statement to a practical public policy is a large step, nowhere well-spelled-out as far as I know. It is pretty clear that some approaches won't work. For example, simply exhorting farmers to conserve water isn't going to work.

There is also a lot of talk about farmers growing too many water intensive crops, like alfalfa and rice. Well, maybe they do. These are issues that are extremely controversial, but must be part of the discussion. The other side argues that cutting the production of certain crops will not increase the cost or production of food crops. We in the Legislature have to look at all sides.

As long as water is inordinately cheap, there is no reason for people to conserve, trade or sell. For many users, particularly those who benefit from the federal project, water prices have not reflected the real cost. What this means is that the market is not allowed to operate to set the price of water given competing interests and the hidden costs which are usually environmental. Serious losses in the fish and other wildlife populations and the clean-up of polluted waters from whatever source are factors that must be considered in future equations, not postponed and isolated from water management decisions.

A proposal that has some merit and acknowledges the disparity of water pricing policies is a water surcharge. Some estimates say we use around 40 million acre-feet of water in California each year. A surcharge of $2.50 per acre-foot would raise $100 million. It would add a negligible amount to the cost paid by users of high-cost water. It would add a lot to the cost of the most underpriced water in the state and stimulate some interest in conservation.

STATE/FEDERAL COOPERATION

California's two most massive water systems, the federal Central Valley Project (CVP) and the State Water Project (SWP), are run under different pricing structures. The federal system is vastly more out of line with real water costs and operates under different allocation rules, not to mention different managements. The much larger federal system is set up under rules that effectively prohibit using its water in southern California, even if a major emergency makes that a good thing to do.

The commitment of the federal system to helping meet state water quality and Delta protection standards is a little grudging. It seems to me that California cannot hope to have a sensible water management policy so long as the vast federal Central Valley system is run separately and incongruously from important parts of state water policy. Drought makes those incongruities all the more glaring.

Two members of Congress, Sen. Bill Bradley and Rep. George Miller, have identified this as a priority. Their efforts to tie CVP operations much more closely into state water policy are not only sensible but essential to any long-term water policy solution.

RESERVOIR MANAGEMENT

This is another of those things that no one really likes to talk about, at least in public. But the truth is, running the reservoirs of a water project involves taking a gamble. There is a trade-off between supplying more water in most years and having water in reserve to get through dry periods.

In 1986, almost exactly as the current dry period was beginning, the state water contractors and DWR changed their bets. The system had been operated conservatively, with quite a bit of water carried over each Fall because of the possibility that the next year or two might be dry.

DWR and the state contractors agreed that the reservoir operating rules were to be changed. There was to be less carryover water each fall. More water was to be supplied to agriculture so that they would not take the cuts that they usually had to take during average years. In a limited way, this was a rational policy but it shifted reservoir management assumptions to a gamble.

In most years, under average rainfall conditions, it would have caused no problems and the SWP would have supplied more water each year. But conditions have not been average, and the current drought has put the downside of this policy in glaring relief. The downside is that there is less water in the reservoirs to get us through really dry years. It seems to me that this "technical" change in the way the state's reservoirs are operated is causing this drought to be harder on Californians than it really needs to be. At a minimum, I think the Legislature needs to look into the way reservoir operations may have amplified the effects of this drought.

NATURAL RESOURCES

One of the more dramatic effects of the drought is to put new strain on the competition between species—the human species versus fish and wildlife. Our innate first reaction during a drought is to worry that there won't be enough water for urban areas and agricultural users. Fish, wildlife and even plant species have claims on water, too. These are legal claims, and the environment has its lawyers. The public trust doctrine is not some vague, theoretical concept. It is established law and must be respected.

Further, many Californians consider the state of our environment and environmental problems to be the most serious issue facing this state. Our natural resources, such as wetlands and the diverse species, have been diminishing at extraordinary rates. Today, only 5 percent of the historic wetlands exist in California.

Even before the drought, the fish were in trouble. Striped bass were declining. The salmon were facing real danger of extinction. The State Water Resources Control Board was under court order to take their responsibilities toward these problems more seriously. Endangered species law was being invoked. In short, a pitched battle was being fought over this most fundamental part of California water law. All of this was occurring before the drought. Now the ecological stakes are escalating with each passing day.

Most important, the heart of the water policy of the state for not only natural resources but for delivery is the Bay-Delta

Estuary. Depending on who you talk to, it is an estuary or a transfer system. It is the site of a major ecological battle between endangered species, water quality and water supply needs. How we solve the Bay-Delta problem signals the resolution of our water policy. It is the microcosm of the competing diverse interests in our state.

Nearly 60 percent of the water exports move through the Delta, over a million recreational users are found there each year, and it serves as the most important wetland resource in the western United States. Today, the Delta is plagued by water flowing uphill due to the enormous power of the export pumps. Reduced flows increase salinity levels which threaten water quality and habitat. The diverse and pivotal role of this resource cannot be underestimated or undervalued.

GROUND WATER

Ground water is our ultimate water insurance, the aquatic bank account that can get us through dry times. It can also be our cheapest reservoir, one we can use with the least likelihood of confrontation and litigation, but only if we are reasonably sensible about taking care of ground water resources.

There are a couple of problems concerning ground water. One has to do with water quality. Many aquifers are contaminated with fuels, solvents, pesticides and other contaminants. They have to be restored, even if it is difficult and expensive. I do not accept the proposition that, because ground water basins are contaminated, we ought to build new surface water supply projects to replace the dirty water. I don't think that is a politically acceptable path, and I suspect it is also an unsafe one.

The other problem is unregulated use and overuse. Ground water practices in nonadjudicated basins are one of those Old West frontier anachronisms that have probably outlived their acceptability. We have been able to avoid doing anything about these practices in large areas of the state for the practical reason that the abundance of water supplied by state and federal water projects took the heat off.

Recent reports indicate that agriculture production and revenues were not devastated by the fifth year of drought. Early in 1991, we heard dire predictions that agriculture would post huge losses in production and revenues. However, we had an unusually wet March which was viewed as a blessing and a curse for agriculture. But the other significant factor was the continued overpumping of ground water by farmers to meet their water needs. My concern is that we could return to many of the ground water problems that we experienced in the 1950s related to overpumping of ground water.

WATER QUALITY

Water quality is also a large and contentious subject, of rapidly increasing importance. Quality standards were set for public health reasons. Clean water is important to everyone in California, including fish and wildlife. Drought or no drought, there ought to be a very strong bias against trifling with water quality standards. Now it may be possible that there are places so dry, where the shortage is so severe, that there is just no other alternative. But I am very concerned when situations become so dire that we trade off human health and wildlife resources.

This is one area where drought experiments do not lead in a direction acceptable for long-term water policy. In fact, the federal Environmental Protection Agency recently disapproved the State Water Resources Control Board's water quality control plan for the Bay-Delta. Unless we develop the appropriate standards, the federal government will do it for us.

However, rule adjustments that encourage reuse of reclaimed water, without threatening human health, are an additional option. Reclamation seems likely to be an important source of long-term water in California.

A related topic is agricultural run-off and drainage. Long considered sacrosanct, these systems must be integrated into our water quality framework. How this is done will be the focus of strenuous debate. But if the urban areas must clean up their contaminated ground water reserves, agriculture must do their part with their used water.

GROWTH

We know that California's population is growing rapidly and that this growth places an additional strain on existing resources. Agriculture argues that they are using the same percentage of water that they used 10 years ago. Urban areas claim expanding suburbs and increasing populations are straining their abilities to provide water.

Growth challenges us to look at all the strategies that I have listed. All of these categories must be strenuously examined and tried before we talk about more plumbing as the only answer to our problems.

The question at some point may be, "Do we need to do something to increase California's net water supply?" Changes in the Delta may be needed. More reservoirs may be needed. Better facilities for moving and storing wet year water may be needed. We will need to look into those things.

Other ideas that require discussion are proposals that would place some pressure on local entities to be more responsible in growth management decisions, for example a requirement that new developments have a guaranteed water supply before the building permits are approved. Perhaps we should mandate that any new starts must use the best available conservation technologies. Nothing is forbidden in this discussion about long-term water policy. Everyone must share the pain and responsibility.

I believe that more plumbing is a last resort. Otherwise, we will not change the way we think about the management and value of this resource. Frankly, I don't believe that I am alone because I believe that is the way the people of California think about it. And the politics of California water must reflect that judgement. As I see it, making fundamental progress on water means making progress in all the areas that I've mentioned.

The alternatives are either complete inaction or continued fruitless water wars, neither of which will be tolerated by the people of this state, who today, more than ever, are focused on this issue. Public awareness is a good thing. I have confidence in the public to sort through even the current Byzantine water policies. You can be sure that they will be playing close attention to any proposed solutions.

Water is not a question of who has the most money to leverage a series of aqueducts and canals anymore. Those days belong to the history books. Our state has come a long way and hard times like today must strengthen our resolve to manage our water wisely. The quality of our lives and the astonishing diversity of our state depends on it.

The California state capitol is the site of many historic water negotiations. Some now believe that consensus and not legislation is the answer to California water problems. But most involved in the process acknowledge that strong leadership from the governor and Legislature is of primary importance to the success of the process. Photo credit: Water Education Foundation.

MEETING THE WATER NEEDS OF CALIFORNIA

Dominic Cortese

When I was appointed chairman of the Assembly Water, Parks and Wildlife Committee, people both congratulated me and gave me their condolences. Fortunately or unfortunately, I am not battle-weary from California's past water wars.

During my tenure as Chairman, water will be defined as a statewide, not a regional or local, resource. Californians need to combine their efforts, regardless of their geographic location, to solve the complex water issues facing us if we are to continue as an economic power into to the 21st century.

HISTORICAL PERSPECTIVE

It is obvious that water and water use in California could provide the basis for a novel of historical proportions that could compete with *How the West was Won.* In fact, this drama continues today and will proceed into the future.

Water use and water quality problems arose early on in the settlement of California. Well over 100 years ago, the discovery of gold drew throngs of gold seekers to early mining communities in California's Sierra Nevada. When the boom years were over, a few lusty stalwarts went to the river edges and directed great

---

Assemblyman Dominic L. Cortese is the chair of the Assembly Committee on Water, Parks and Wildlife.

water cannons (monitors) at the banks and hillsides in an effort to retrieve the glittering reward from the dislodged sand and gravels.

Although large quantities of gold were retrieved, the hydraulic mines annually discharged 600,000 cubic yards of silt and debris. This large load of silt and debris soon choked the American and Sacramento rivers and significantly impacted water quality as far down as San Francisco Bay. In turn, this impaired navigability, fouled waters and angered the public. The political turmoil that followed reached the California Supreme Court in *People v. Gold Run D.& E. Co.,* (1884) 66 Cal. 132 [4 P. 1152] which held that an injunction should issue, based upon the belief that the rights of the people in navigable rivers were paramount and that any intrusion upon that right constituted a nuisance. This decision virtually led to the demise of hydraulic mining in California when the Legislature responded by enacting Public Resources Code Section 2602 declaring that hydraulic mining could only be carried on without material injury to navigable streams or the lands adjacent thereto. Later legislative enactments (Public Resources Code Section 2555 and 2558) required further precautions to protect water supplies for human consumption.

The Legislature, concerned with the decline in fish populations, enacted a number of statutes to protect water resources and public trust resources well before the authorizations and impacts of the federal Central Valley Project (CVP) and the State Water Project (SWP). The early statutes were related to protecting anadromous fisheries from pollution (Fish and Game Code Section 5650), obstruction in river for fish passage, (Fish and Game Code Section 5600 et.seq.) and protection of gravels for spawning. In *People v. Truckee River Lumber Co.,* (1897) 116 Cal. 397, 399-400 the court held that a pulp mill operating on the river placed deleterious refuse in such a stream, poisoning the waters and thereby killing fish; that such acts were a public nuisance, and the state's authority to protect its sovereign rights in fish extends to all waters within the state, public or private. The concern of the Legislature and the public for water quality and protection of fish in the waters of the state is steeped in history and tradition predating the massive water development and competing uses to come.

THE GREAT WATER PROJECTS

The CVP was authorized under the Rivers and Harbors Act of 1937. The initial units consisted of Shasta Dam on the Sacramento River and Friant Dam on the San Joaquin River. As part of the initial conveyance system, the Contra Costa, Delta Mendota, Friant, Kern and Madera canals were contracted between the periods 1940 to 1951. Today there are 23 dams and reservoirs and hundred of miles of canals supplying about 7 million acre-feet of water to 2.8 million irrigated acres of land.

Perhaps the most dramatic example of unmitigated impacts caused by the CVP in its initial operation was the elimination of the chinook salmon from the main San Joaquin River, which had supported one of the state's largest runs. In 1946, the fate of the fish was sealed with water storage and virtual elimination of continuous flow below Friant Dam—a boon for irrigated agriculture but a bust for fish. In the rush to justify expansion of the California water storage facilities, fisheries protection laws were to fall from public view. In fact, by the time the Bureau of Reclamation applied for the water rights to operate Friant Dam, the salmon run no longer existed. Basically, the State Water Resources Control Board issued the water permits without any provision for flows to maintain fish and wildlife resource on the grounds it was a fait-accompli.

A 1951 opinion by then-Attorney General Edmund G. "Pat" Brown held that the flow release requirements of the Fish and Game Code was not a reservation of water for fish but was a rule for operation of dams if there was enough water left to release below the dam. This view has been since refuted by the attorney general's office and overturned by court decisions. An attempt by the Department of Fish and Game to appeal the adverse decision of the State Water Resources Control Board was withdrawn under pressure from the governor's office in 1959.

At the time, there was not great public concern over withdrawals of water from the Delta since the volumes were large and the San Joaquin salmon run was primarily of local interest, a stark contrast to the environmental concern and public trust attitude of today. Consensus among interest groups was not an issue at the time.

The SWP was authorized by the Burns-Porter Act ratified by the voters in 1960. The act authorized $1.75 billion dollars in funds to implement the SWP and was hotly contested at the time. The measure was passed by 51 percent voter approval. The genesis of the SWP authorization was the State Central Valley Project Act of 1933 which identified "The Feather River and Sacramento-San Joaquin Delta Diversion Projects."

The water system for the SWP follows the same general path as the CVP and was principally designed to carry and transport water from northern to southern California. The initial facilities included Oroville Dam and Reservoir, San Luis Dam (joint federal-state facility), the South and North Bay Aqueducts and the California Aqueduct. The principal transportation facility of the SWP is the California Aqueduct which carries project waters to the San Joaquin Valley and population centers in southern California. Currently, the SWP is comprised of more than 20 dams and reservoirs and associated power plants, pumping plants and more than 100 miles of branch aqueducts. Additional facilities are now under construction, including the installation of four additional pumps at its Delta pumping facility to help meet current demands. Dependable water supply from the SWP is about 2.4 million acre-feet. Requests for water from various sources is about 3.0 million acre-feet with a projected 4.0 million or more acre-feet by the year 2010.

The Burns-Porter Act paved the way for the continued development of the SWP. The concepts of storing water during times of surplus and providing water to areas of deficiency in the state was being implemented. The die was cast and in the 1960s a growing public concern was reflected regarding the combined impact of the CVP and SWP together. However, no one could predict at the time the water quality degradation and impact to fish and wildlife resources of the Delta.

The Sacramento-San Joaquin Delta is at the center of the CVP and SWP system operationally and geographically. The Delta can be described as a switchyard for water management purposes where water is routed through a complex transportation system. No water problem in California has generated more controversy and has involved more investigation and studies than water issues in the Sacramento-San Joaquin Delta. Simply put, water is conveyed from northern California through the Delta and transported to water-deficient areas in the south. Water not captured or diverted upstream or in the Delta flows west through Carquinez Straits to San Francisco Bay and through the Golden Gate. The drainage basin of the San Francisco Bay system covers over 40 percent of the land area of California. Ninety percent of the total surface flow enters the bay via the Sacramento and San Joaquin rivers. The mixing of the two rivers occurs in the Delta immediately east of Suisun Bay and is generally termed Delta outflow. The Delta has large cultivated islands that were originally reclaimed from marsh land. These islands are surrounded by approximately 700 miles of interwoven channels of varying width and depth. Significant marsh areas that remain are Suisun Marsh, Northern San Pablo Bay and South San Francisco Bay.

Fresh water enters the Delta from the Sacramento and San Joaquin rivers. Fresh water flows mix with incoming salt water tidal flows from the ocean tides into San Francisco Bay. The mixing of salt water with fresh water from the Sacramento and San Joaquin rivers creates a transition (so-called entrapment zone) or salinity gradient that extends from northern San Francisco Bay to the western Delta.

Historically, during extremely wet years fresh water flows have extended as far as the Golden Gate, while in extremely dry years salt water has extended almost to Sacramento. This zone creates conditions of extremely high biological productivity. Many fish species spawn in or pass through the area and are dependent on food production and the gradual change in salinity to accommodate their physiological adaption from fresh water to salt water and vice-versa. Likewise, the distribution of wetland and marsh vegetation and water quality conditions vary with the circulation pattern, primarily Delta outflow.

Presently, Delta outflow is controlled to a large extent by various water project developments that change volume and flow in the estuary. By far, the CVP and SWP have the largest impact, at times diverting up to 40 percent or more of the inflow through the large pumps located in the southern Delta. Since only about 10 percent of the flow comes from the San Joaquin River at the south end of the Delta, most of the water is transported from the north through various channels and a condition frequently exists when pumping causes western and southern Delta channels to flow backwards, the so-called "reverse flows."

The impact of water development projects on the Sacramento-San Joaquin Delta and San Francisco Bay systems are so complex that they almost defy comprehension. Millions of dollars have already been spent on studies and data collection with the expectation that substantial funding will be required to continue these efforts in the future. There are major problems in need of a solution associated with Delta water transfer and diversion. Even though many positive actions have been taken, the most severe remain to be solved.

In the early 1960s, during the initial evaluation of the SWP, several adverse impacts resulting from Delta diversion were identified. They included: concerns for loss of small fish and eggs at the diversion intakes; impact of reverse flows in the southern Delta on upstream and downstream migrant fish, particularly salmon, steelhead, striped bass and American shad; reduction of fish food organisms because of high flow rates in the Delta channels; changes in the salinity gradient in important nursery areas and waterfowl habitat. Almost three decades later these problems are still with us, including critical water quality problems that relate to agricultural and drinking water supplies. Recent findings indicate potential problems with the formation of carcinogenic trihalomethanes (THMs) when chlorine used for disinfecting drinking water combine with bromides in Delta waters. State and federal water standards may impose serious constraints on the use of Delta water for drinking.

There appears to be a consensus among major interest groups, including agricultural, environmental, municipal, industrial and recreational, that the status quo will result in continued degradation of fish and wildlife and water quality of the Delta. Positive action must be initiated to alleviate existing problems, restore degraded fish and wildlife resources and protect Delta water quality of the future.

ENVIRONMENTAL PROTECTION AND PUBLIC INTEREST

The Public Trust Doctrine emanates from ancient Roman concepts. English common law adopted the notion of public trust in navigable waters and determined that the Crown owned the beds of navigable waterways in trust for the public. English courts generally limited protection to tidal navigable waters but included rights of egress and regress, for fishing, trading and other uses claimed by the public.

The public trust doctrine in the United States developed concurrently with the country's growth and dependence on the use of extensive waterways for navigation, commerce and fishing. The United States courts have extended the public trust doctrine to include all waters that are "navigable in fact", whether fresh water or salt water.

Basic elements that have been crucial in the development of the doctrine in the United States, and by extension in California, are the consideration of: waterways encompassed within the term navigable; the trust values protected; the identification and extension from the traditional commerce, navigation and fishing trust values protected; and the limitation on government to alienate trust lands and associated values. A number of legal commentators view the public trust as a state law concept based upon the rationale that the federal government held the land under navigable waters in trust for the public and upon admission their lands vested in the states as a fundamental function of state sovereignty (so called equal footing doctrine). The California Supreme Court in *Marks v. Whitney* (1971)

98 Cal. Rptr. 790, 6 Cal., dealing with tidelands in Tomales Bay, expanded the values protected by the public trust doctrine to include "the preservation of those lands in their natural state, so that they may serve as ecological units for scientific study, as open space, and as environments which provide food and habitat for birds and marine life, and which favorably affect the scenery and climate of the area." Further, this decision left the door ajar for application of additional public uses to future decisions. "[T]he public uses to which tidelands are subject are sufficiently flexible to encompass changing public needs."

Court decisions and legislation have supplemented the traditional public trust doctrine into the area of appropriation of water. The most famous (or infamous, depending on your point of view) are the Mono Lake and Bay Delta water decision cases. The issues raised in these cases will undoubtedly be a focal point for future decisions impacting water allocations in the future.

The California Supreme Court in *National Audubon Society v. Superior Court* (1983) 33 Cal. 3d 419 established the role of the public trust doctrine in the California water rights system and explicitly limited those private and governmental actions that would destroy or extinguish public trust resources. Further, the Legislature has granted to the State Water Resources Control Board (SWRCB) the power to issue water rights permits even though the diversion of "water does not promote and may unavoidably harm trust uses at the source stream". However, the state has a duty to protect trust uses whenever it is feasible. The limitation on the SWRCB's power is that the state must bear in mind its trustee duty to consider the effect of an undertaking and "preserve insofar as consistent with public interest the uses protected by the trust." Thus, the SWRCB makes public interest determinations in addition to making findings of fact on the availability of supply for appropriation. In California, unlike many other western states, there exists no vested or property interest for instream flows. Two appellate decisions have interpreted Article X, Section 2 of the California Constitution to require a physical diversion of water in order to create a legal entitlement to the use of water.

The SWRCB issues appropriative permits and licenses, makes "reasonable and beneficial use" determinations, makes findings of fact on the availability of supply for appropriations and makes public trust determinations, all under the concept of "balancing." Some critics contend the balancing process, as applied by the SWRCB, has not worked in protecting fish and wildlife resources and water quality of the Delta and other waterways of the state. Some recent examples cited are: the federal Environmental Protection Agency rejection of water quality standards proposed for the Delta; Natural Resources Defense Counsel, et al., suit in federal court challenging the United States decision to renew the water supply contracts for the Friant unit of the CVP, amended to add state law claims under the public trust doctrine; the U.S. Fish and Wildlife Service petition to list the Delta smelt as a threatened species; the listing of winter run chinook salmon as threatened (federal) and endangered (state), and the all-time low striped bass population.

There is a view that in Article X, Section 2 of the California Constitution, which mandates that "water resources of the state be put to beneficial use to the fullest extent of which they are capable," there is an implied limit to the biological and physical ability of a river to be used consumptively. The application of this "capability" clause provides a rational basis to allocate baseline flows in the rivers and waters of the state in order to sustain water quality and fish and wildlife resources. The "no harm rule" would apply to fish and wildlife equally with other statutorily identified beneficial uses and would establish a limit on diversions that would otherwise destroy or extinguish public trust uses. It will be interesting to see if this view is pursued in future litigation and perhaps even in the formulation of future legislation.

In any event, the growing public concern for environmental quality, aesthetics, clean water, recreation and fish and wildlife will certainly continue to drive public trust issues to the forefront in the area of water use and policy.

FUTURE OPTIONS/ACTIONS

The anticipated growth in California's population to 40 million by the year 2010 and the increasing demand and competition for water to accommodate those needs will indeed tax the creative abilities and negotiation skills of present and future administrations and legislatures.

Some of the current and future options proposed to meet the water needs of a growing population and the environment are now:

* Water conservation should be the foundation for all water use in California. Creative water management measures can be effective in reducing the net use of water. In urban areas such actions as the mandatory installation of low water use appliances and drought-resistant or non-water using landscapes have been effective. In agriculture, improved delivery systems, development of more efficient irrigation methods and changes in crop patterns, where feasible, are all potential water savers.

* Water reclamation/recycling involves the reuse of treated water for various purposes, such as crop and landscape watering, industrial cooling and ground water recharge. Water reclamation is drought-resistant; even during drought periods reclaimed water can be made available for reuse. There are public health concerns and the construction of separate facilities can be costly, but it is estimated that in excess of 600,000 acre-feet of water could be obtained with projects now in the concept, planning, design and construction phases.

* Conjunctive use involves coordinating the use of ground water supplies with available surface supplies. It is a cost-effective and efficient method of water management. It is especially important in the San Joaquin Valley and southern California where ground water use is most intensive. Recharging ground water basins with excess surface water during wet years provides the flexibility to meet water needs in dry years. Many local and

regional water agencies are increasingly involved in ground water recharge projects. DWR sponsors pilot projects and supervises a low-interest loan program authorized by the Water Conservation and Water Quality Bond Law of 1986.

* Alternative water development—traditional water development meant the construction of dams and major water conveyance systems. With the construction of the CVP and SWP, most of the necessary plumbing is in place. Most interests would agree that high costs and the present political climate limits options for new projects. However, some promising considerations are the Los Banos Grandes Reservoir and the Kern Water Bank. Water will be diverted to these offstream projects during the winter months in wet years, storing it for use later in the year or during dry year cycles. These are the types of alternative developments that encourage conservation, transfers and conjunctive use and perhaps are not as controversial as traditional water development because they provide incremental improvements in the current system.

* Water transfer and marketing involve the sale or exchange of water or water rights between individuals or agencies. The success of water transfers is based on the availability of water, the ability to transfer it, the potential benefits and the lack of adverse effects on other parties, such as downstream riparian users, and impacts on fish and wildlife resources and water quality. The concept of marketing water as a commodity has gained acceptance by a diverse number of interest groups. The Water Code declares it to be state policy to facilitate the voluntary transfer of water and water rights and directs DWR, SWRCB and other appropriate agencies to encourage the voluntary transfer of water. The SWRCB is responsible for approval of transfers, DWR is involved in moving water through the state conveyance system, and the Department of Fish and Game is involved in determining the effects of transfers on fish and wildlife.

There is a critical need to improve Delta water transfer efficiency and control salinity intrusion. As noted before, fisheries declines and water quality continue to be major issues. At this point, there are no single solutions to the problem. It will require full coordination and cooperation from a multitude of federal, state and local agencies working together to resolve engineering, environmental and political problems and disputes.

WATER MANAGEMENT POLICY/CONSENSUS

The issues discussed above are but a few of the actions and options that need to be pursued to help solve California's water problems. Many positive actions are in place today, such as the federal/state Coordinated Operation Agreement, wild and scenic river protections, the Suisun Marsh Preservation Agreement, and the Delta Levee Restoration and Protection Project. Much has yet to be accomplished in areas of toxic waste, water quality and protection of fish and wildlife resources.

A new water policy must be formulated which takes into account the interdependence of water needs throughout the state. Water allocation or reallocation must be a statewide concern, and will continue to be one of the most controversial issues before us in the future.

The drought has taught us all a lesson. We should not forget that planning and the formation of consensus among all water users is critical. We must recognize that continued debate does not solve problems. California must come to grips with the longstanding environmental degradation caused in part by water development and insist that environmental protection be an integral component in the solution to California's water future.

The Edmund G. "Pat" Brown Institute of Public Affairs

The "Pat" Brown Institute is an independent non-partisan center of public affairs located on the campus of California State University, Los Angeles. Charged with carrying out the urban mission of the University and the ideals of former Governor Pat Brown, the Institute sponsors forums, applied research, and publications on important and timely issues impacting upon California and its increasingly diverse communities.

The "Pat" Brown Institute affiliated with Cal State Los Angeles in 1987 under the guiding belief that a well-informed public will be able to better prepare for the needs of the present and future. The primary goal of the Institute is to create more effective means of communication and dialogue among public and private sector communities. The Institute aims to create a bridge to provide opportunities for scholars, students and citizens to debate public policy issues.

To realize this goal, the "Pat" Brown Institute has identified four broad research and policy interest areas:

*Governance and Representation
*Social Well-Being
*Economy and Infrastructure
*Natural Resources and the Environment

Programs designed to carry the goals and objectives of the Institute into fruition include:

*Forum and Conference Series
*Applied Research Program
*Publications Program
*Student Internship Program
*Faculty Fellows Program
*Distinguished Lecturer Program
*Public Policy Award Program

The Institute has sponsored and co-sponsored a number of **conferences and symposia** on topics ranging from California's health insurance crisis, solid waste management, and local effects of international trade agreements to civil rights in America, local level redistricting, and tensions among communities of color in Southern California.

Applied research projects of the Institute include studies of demographic, socioeconomic and representation changes in selected cities of the San Valley, the modern history of economic development policymaking priorities in the City of Los Angeles, gang violence in Southern California, and redistricting and representation scenarios and battles in the city and county of Los Angeles.

The "Pat" Brown Institute publishes significant works in three forms: Occasional Papers (reviewed through a scholarly refereed process), Monographs, and Books. The **Publishing Program** of the Institute began in 1989. Publications include *Achieving Consensus on Water Policy in California, California Initiatives and Referendums, Emergency Disaster Management, Minority Political Empowerment, Gang Violence Prevention*, and *Ethics Reform at the Municipal Level.*

In serving as a bridge between university and community, the Institute is coordinating a seven-campus **California State University Urban Coalition** effort to provide educational services and resources matching the needs of inner-city communities of the Los Angeles Basin.

"Pat" Brown Institute **Student Internships** are of three types: research internships, public sector internships, and community service internships. Research interns work with designated faculty on the Institute's applied research projects. Public Sector interns are placed in the offices of public officials or in agencies of regional government. Community Service interns are placed in community based organizations or legal advocacy organizations.

Faculty Fellows, primarily in the California State University system, will be granted released time from teaching duties to direct applied research projects over a designated period of time. Such awards will be primarily based on grant opportunities funded through the Institute.

The "Pat" Brown Institute wishes to honor those who have been major contributors to public life in California. Recipients of the Institute's Local and State-based **Public Policy Awards** will be honored at the Institute's annual dinner traditionally held on the occasion of former Governor Pat Brown's birthday.

The campus setting of the "Pat" Brown Institute, housed in the John F. Kennedy Memorial Library, provides a wealth of resources and an expanded range of programs. The University's schools and departments provide an environment which complements and enhances the research work and other programs of the Institute. Faculty members and students, in particular, from Cal State L.A. and other campuses of the California State University system, are key Institute resources.

For more information about the "Pat" Brown Institute, please call or write:

The Edmund G. "Pat" Brown Institute of Public Affairs
California State University, Los Angeles
Library South, Room 4056
5151 State University Drive
Los Angeles, CA 90032-8261
(213) 343-3770 FAX: (213) 343-3774